# A Guide to Spatial History

## Areas, Aspects, and Avenues of Research

Konrad Lawson, Riccardo Bavaj and Bernhard Struck

Open access directly online plus EPUB and PDF downloads available at:
<https://spatialhistory.net/guide>

ISBN: 978-1-7371368-1-1 (e-book)

Published by Olsokhagen Publishing

Cover image:
Marshallese Navigational Stick Chart (A926.1)
© Denver Museum of Nature & Science

# CONTENTS

# ACKNOWLEDGMENTS

We would like to thank Alexander Akin, Fiona Banham, Alex Burkhardt, John Clark, Tim Cresswell, Sarah Easterby-Smith, Diarmid Finnegan, Vahishtai Debashish Ghosh, Dawn Hollis, Lauren Holmes, James Koranyi, Jacqueline Rose, and Lauren Nicole Vaughan for help, comments, and insights.

# Introduction

This guide provides an overview of the thematic areas, analytical aspects, and avenues of research which, together, form a broader conversation around doing spatial history. Spatial history is not a field with clearly delineated boundaries. For the most part, it lacks a distinct, unambiguous scholarly identity. It can only be thought of in relation to other, typically more established fields. Indeed, one of the most valuable utilities of spatial history is its capacity to facilitate conversations across those fields. Consequently, it must be discussed in relation to a variety of historiographical contexts. Each of these have their own intellectual genealogies, institutional settings, and conceptual path dependencies. Any attempt to approach spatial history in a hermetic way, as if it existed in a historiographical vacuum, would run counter to its very purpose. Spatial history is not merely one among many 'hyphenated' fields.[1] It does not aim at further compartmentalization. At its very core lies a heightened sensitivity to the spatial dimensions of history *in general*. Historians may or may not choose to explicitly adopt the label 'spatial history'. Either way, there exists a sizeable body of *spatially attuned* historical scholarship that is eminently worthy of discussion.

This guide may be fruitfully read alongside the edited volume *Doing Spatial History*, edited by Riccardo Bavaj, Konrad Lawson, and Bernhard Struck.[2] Divided into three parts, this volume offers fifteen case studies, with different entry points to the field: The first part provides examples of how to make use of specific kinds of historical sources such as maps, travel guides, and architectural drawings. The second part explores specific kinds of spaces, ranging from ships, to bars, and border zones. The final part contains chapters on concepts, tools and approaches such as 'Lefebvrean landscapes', 'maritoriality', and digital mapping methods. In his introduction to the volume, Riccardo Bavaj provides an overview of the wide variety of 'spatial history', and traces its development from key early figures through the 'spatial turn' across multiple disciplines. Bavaj sees the value of 'spatial history' in its ability 1) to serve as a 'signpost for historians to find inspiration in relevant cognate fields', 2) to 'facilitate conversations *among* historians of different hues and

---

[1] 'Über Räume und Register der Geschichtsschreibung: Ein Gespräch mit Karl Schlögel', *Zeithistorische Forschungen/Studies in Contemporary History* 1, 2004, 396-413, here 402.

[2] Riccardo Bavaj, Konrad Lawson and Bernhard Struck (eds.), *Doing Spatial History*, London and New York: Routledge, 2022.

specializations', and 3) to create new knowledge through a shared interdisciplinary perspective and a common analytical focus on 'space' and 'place'.

If *Doing Spatial History* offers an introduction to the field followed by multiple case studies, this guide aims to give readers a stronger historiographical appreciation for the broad range of spatially attentive scholarship. Most of the works surveyed here were not authored by self-designated 'spatial historians'. To be sure, many of these contributions share a common analytical focus on 'space' and 'place'. Others, however, prefer cognate concepts such as 'landscape', 'nature', and the 'urban environment'. Moreover, some of this scholarship does not engage with spatial theory in any explicit, self-conscious way. And yet all of the works included in this guide can meaningfully inform a dialogue on the spatial dimensions of history.

Needless to say, our coverage is by no means comprehensive. It cannot possibly be so. Nor is it an outline for a 'Great Books programme', or an attempt to build a sort of 'spatial history canon'. Such an enterprise would run contrary to the very notion of spatial history as an 'expansive field'. This guide is not meant to provide a definitive capstone. It serves as a possible springboard for a broader conversation.

Usually, the introductory part of a guide of this kind would be the proper place to articulate a compelling rationale behind the choice of areas, themes, and approaches. We might expect the usual invocations of the inevitably 'timely' and the seemingly 'perennial'. However, such rhetorical veils have worn thin. We frankly acknowledge the limited range of this guide. We offer neither a bird's eye view nor a view from nowhere. What follows is informed by our respective academic socialisations, and by geographical as well as intellectual positionalities. This guide includes a section on 'spaces of knowledge', which invites readers to reflect on the spatial conditionality of knowledge production. This guide is itself place-bound. To pretend otherwise would be to ignore a fundamental insight of spatial history.

Examples are drawn, in part, from our own research interests and teaching experiences. These are mainly situated in the history of Europe and East Asia from the late eighteenth to the twentieth century. At the same time, we have attempted to enter into the spirit of boundary spanning and to go beyond our individual comfort zones. We have drawn on the idea of spatial history as a translation aid in order to bring in perspectives from cognate disciplines. Readers may also want to browse the extensive endnote section for geographical areas and thematic aspects not covered in the text. With that said, however, many will note the absence of dedicated sections on, for instance, spaces of trade, commerce and consumption,[3] sacred spaces,[4] places of memory,[5] and the large domain of spatial literary studies.[6]

We recognize that readers' expectations will vary considerably. Some may never have heard of the term 'spatial history', while others may have come across it in very specific contexts. These might range from historical geographic information systems (GIS) to particular subject areas such as Eastern European

---

[3] See, especially, Jon Stobart, Andrew Hann and Victoria Morgan, *Spaces of Consumption: Leisure and Shopping in the English Town, c.1680-1830*, London and New York: Routledge, 2007; Jon Stobart and Mark Rothery, *Consumption and the Country House*, Oxford: Oxford University Press, 2016; Frank Mort, *Cultures of Consumption: Masculinities and Social Space in Late Twentieth-Century Britain*, London and New York: Routledge, 1996.

[4] See, for example, Veronica della Dora, *Landscape, Nature, and the Sacred in Byzantium*, Cambridge University Press, 2016; Sandra E. Greene, *Sacred Sites and the Colonial Encounter: A History of Meaning and Memory in Ghana*, Bloomington: Indiana University Press, 2002; Will Coster and Andrew Spicer (eds.), *Sacred Space in Early Modern Europe*, Cambridge: Cambridge University Press, 2005; Andrew Spicer and Sarah Hamilton (eds.), *Defining the Holy: Sacred Space in Medieval and Early Modern Europe*, London and New York: Routledge, 2005; James Robson, *Power of Place: The Religious Landscape of the Southern Sacred Peak (Nanyue) in Medieval China*, Cambridge, Mass.: Harvard University Asia Center, 2009; Yoshiko Imaizumi, *Sacred Space in the Modern City: The Fractured Pasts of Meiji Shrine, 1912-1958*, Leiden and Boston: Brill, 2013.

[5] See, for instance, Sarah De Nardi et al. (eds.), *The Routledge Handbook of Memory and Place*, London and New York: Routledge, 2020; Danielle Drozdzewski, Sarah De Nardi and Emma Waterton (eds.), *Memory, Place and Identity: Commemoration and Remembrance of War and Conflict*, London and New York: Routledge, 2016; as well as the exemplary works by Nuala C. Johnson, *Ireland, the Great War and the Geography of Remembrance*, Cambridge: Cambridge University Press, 2003; Karen E. Till, *The New Berlin: Memory, Politics, Place*, Minneapolis: University of Minnesota Press, 2005; Jay Winter, *Sites of Memory, Sites of Mourning: The Great War in European Cultural History*, Cambridge: Cambridge University Press, 1998; James E. Young, *The Texture of Memory: Holocaust Memorials and Meaning*, New Haven: Yale University Press, 1993.

[6] See, above all, the wide-ranging work by Robert T. Tally Jr. (ed.), *Spatial Literary Studies: Interdisciplinary Approaches to Space, Geography and the Imagination*, New York and London: Routledge, 2021; id. (ed.), *Teaching Space, Place, and Literature*, London and New York: Routledge, 2018; id. (ed.), *The Routledge Handbook of Literature and Space*, London and New York: Routledge, 2017; id. (ed.), *Literary Cartographies: Spatiality, Representation, and Narrative*, Basingstoke: Palgrave Macmillan, 2014; id., *Topophrenia: Place, Narrative, and the Spatial Imagination*, Bloomington: Indiana University Press, 2019; see also Anders Engberg-Pedersen (ed.), *Literature and Cartography: Theories, Histories, Genres*, Cambridge, Mass. and London: MIT Press, 2017; Jon Hegglund, *World Views: Metageographies of Modernist Fiction*, Oxford: Oxford University Press, 2012; Anne Lounsbery, *Life Is Elsewhere: Symbolic Geography in the Russian Provinces, 1800-1917*, Ithaca: Cornell University Press, 2019; Andrew Thacker, *Modernism, Space and the City*, Edinburgh: Edinburgh University Press, 2019; Russell West-Pavlov, *Eastern African Literatures: Towards an Aesthetics of Proximity*, Oxford: Oxford University Press, 2018; Eric B. White, *Transatlantic Avant-Gardes: Little Magazines and Localist Modernism*, Edinburgh: Edinburgh University Press, 2013; Bertrand Westphal, *Geocriticism: Real and Fictional Spaces*, New York: Palgrave Macmillan, 2011, French 2007; and the earlier works by J. Hillis Miller, *Topographies*, Stanford: California University Press, 1995; and Franco Moretti, *Atlas of the European Novel, 1800-1900*, London and New York: Verso, 1998.

history, which has seen much spatially attuned research in recent decades.[7] The 'spatial turn' manifested itself differently, and at different times, across both national and (sub)disciplinary boundaries. No doubt, there are many 'varieties of spatial history'. From our perspective, and in our engagement with spatial approaches to history, however, some intellectual lineages appear more prominent than others. These have been foregrounded in this guide. This is not intended to imply a judgment on the intellectual viability of other, unmentioned approaches, or approaches solely covered in the endnotes. Readers are encouraged to consult the handbooks and companions listed in the reference section of the introduction to the volume *Doing Spatial History* for a fuller picture of spatial thinkers and lines of thought.

Regardless of any subject-specific antecedents and trajectories, the individual sections of this guide reflect many of the general trends, and force fields, delineated in the introduction to *Doing Spatial History*: especially the 'cultural turn' in 1980s Anglo-American geography, with its growing emphasis on 'meaning', 'vision', and 'text', but also the tension between 'mind and matter', i.e. the relationship, and interdependency, between the constructedness and materiality of space.

This guide is based on the idea of spatial history as a common forum which serves to link several pertinent fields. These include environmental history, landscape history, local and regional history, transnational and global history, urban history, architectural history, the history of cartography, and the history of science. With this in mind, we survey the following areas: territoriality, infrastructure, and borders; nature, environment, and landscape; city and home; social space and political protest; spaces of knowledge; spatial imaginaries; cartographic representations; and historical GIS research.

All the sections below follow a similar structure. First, they give an idea of where a field originated and how it evolved. Following this, they provide glimpses into the relevant research landscape. The examples chosen here tend to be indicative rather than representative of a certain area, trend or approach.

---

[7] See, for instance, Mark Bassin, Christopher Ely and Melissa K. Stockdale (eds.), *Space, Place, and Power in Modern Russia: Essays in the New Spatial History*, DeKalb: Northern Illinois University Press, 2010; David Crowley and Susan E. Reid (eds.), *Socialist Spaces: Sites of Everyday Life in the Eastern Bloc*, Oxford and New York: Berg, 2002; Evgeny Dobrenko and Eric Naiman (eds.), *The Landscape of Stalinism: The Art and Ideology of Soviet Space*, Seattle and London: University of Washington Press, 2003; Karl Schlögel (ed.), *Mastering Russian Spaces: Raum und Raumbewältigung als Probleme der russischen Geschichte*, Munich: R. Oldenbourg Verlag, 2011; see also Frances Nethercott, *Writing History in Late Imperial Russia: Scholarship and the Literary Canon*, London: Bloomsbury, 2020, pp. 117-37, for early Russian precursors to spatial history.

Often, a particular facet of a given work is highlighted to this effect. Several works, of course, may fit into more than one category. Finally, each section concludes by offering a synoptic outline of a key work in the field. All of these selected key works have become central reference points in their respective fields. Most of them were trailblazing pieces of original research at the time of publication, such as Anssi Paasi's *Territories, Boundaries, and Consciousness* (1996), Brenda Yeoh's *Contesting Space in Colonial Singapore* (1996), and Thongchai Winichakul's *Siam Mapped* (1994). Other contributions are more clearly works of synthesis and provide effective entry points to a scholarly discussion, such as David Livingstone's *Putting Science in Its Place* (2003).

# 1 Territoriality, Infrastructure, and Borders

The end of the Cold War gave rise to a renewed sense of geo-historical contingency, and thus to 'the spatial turn'. The Soviet Union's collapse triggered processes of de- and reterritorialization. Borders were redrawn and supranational bonds rebuilt. This re-sensitized scholars to the historical conditionality of geopolitical constellations. Of course, and as the attentive reader will notice, the introduction to *Doing Spatial History* already elaborates on the significance of the end of the Cold War for 'the spatial turn'. It is nonetheless worth reiterating here. So too is the connection between, on the one hand, 'the spatial turn' and, on the other, the transformation of communication technologies, digital networks, and infrastructure, as well as the acceleration of global economic transactions. From around 1990, these trends fed into a discourse on the alleged 'end of the nation-state' and the rise of a seemingly 'borderless world'. As the introduction to *Doing Spatial History* makes clear, these contentions did not go unchallenged – far from it. The key point here, however, is that the emerging discourse on 'globalization' – whatever its inner complexities – made an important contribution to the rising interest in space.[8]

*Once within Borders* is the title of a major work of synthesis by Harvard historian Charles Maier. It was published in 2016, but its origins lay in the more immediate aftermath of the Cold War, as well as turn-of-the-millennium debates on 'globalization'. During this period, Maier carved out what would become the book's conceptual and analytical framework. The focus lies on territoriality – and territorial transformations – over the past five centuries. Maier delineates an era of 'modern territoriality', a period marked by a near-complete overlap between, on the one hand, the 'decision space' of rule, law and governance and, on the other, the 'identity space' of principal loyalties and belonging. The final quarter of the twentieth century, Maier argues, has seen the curtain begin to fall on this era of 'modern territoriality'. Territoriality has ceased to be a self-evident, 'taken-for-granted' category. It is thus ripe for historicization.

---

[8] See, for instance, the important article by Saskia Sassen, 'Spatialities and Temporalities of the Global: Elements for a Theorization', *Public Culture* 12, 2000, 215-32; for an important work at the intersection of global history and spatial history, see Jürgen Osterhammel's magnum opus *The Transformation of the World: A Global History of the Nineteenth Century*, Princeton: Princeton University Press, 2014, German 2009.

Despite the book's title, however, Maier commences with the idea that 'once', in other, earlier historical settings, human beings had *not* lived 'within borders'. In Europe, this began to change from the seventeenth century, and especially so with the nineteenth-century formation of nation-states. Increasingly, people came to live within the bounded spaces of nation-states. At the end of the book, Maier offers some reflections which seem again to stand in contradiction to the volume's title. He points to more recent boundary-reinforcing historical developments such as statesmen erecting fences and building walls. This gives him cause to ask whether people might not, after all, '*still*' be living 'within borders' – that is, in national territories that are 'still guarded, still militant'.[9]

Since 'the spatial turn', historians have addressed the subject of territoriality in a more sustained and systematic manner.[10] Maier defines territory as 'space with a border that allows effective control of public and political life'. In this context, effective control means exclusive control. In modern times, this control has been exerted or facilitated by political decision makers, fortress architects, urban planners, civil engineers, land surveyors, cartographers, and geopolitical pundits. Territory is understood as 'turf', carved out from 'global space', so to speak, in order to establish and exert political authority. Politics, then, operates through claims over the management of space. The history of territory is thus the history of 'political space'.[11]

---

[9] Charles S. Maier, *Once within Borders: Territories of Power, Wealth, and Belonging since 1500*, Cambridge, Mass.: Harvard University Press, 2016, pp. 3-4, 277-9 (own emphasis); id., 'Consigning the Twentieth Century to History: Alternative Narratives for the Modern Era', *American Historical Review*, 105, 2000, 807-31, here 808 (with fn. 2), 816, 823, 829; see also id., 'Leviathan 2.0: Inventing Modern Statehood', in Emily S. Rosenberg (ed.), *A World Connecting, 1870-1945*, Cambridge, Mass.: Harvard University Press, 2012, pp. 29-282.

[10] Traditionally, Maier states, 'geographers and social theorists have written about territory, spatiality, and [...] place; historians about territories, but not about territory as such.' From the perspective of Robert Mayhew, a historical geographer and intellectual historian, Maier's book demonstrates the importance of 'writing spatial history' by placing rather well-known historical material in 'unfamiliar conjunctions', and by approaching it from 'different angles'. Charles S. Maier, 'Transformations of Territoriality, 1600-2000', in Gunilla Budde, Sebastian Conrad and Oliver Janz (eds.), *Transnationale Geschichte: Themen, Tendenzen und Theorien*, Göttingen: Vandenhoeck & Ruprecht, 2006, pp. 32-55, here p. 35; Robert Mayhew, 'Context Is Everything', *Times Literary Supplement*, 7 April 2017; see also Jessica Wang, 'Reckoning with the Spatial Turn: Cartography, Territoriality, and International History', *Diplomatic History* 41, 2017, 1010-8.

[11] Maier, 'Transformations of Territoriality', pp. 34, 36; id., *Once within Borders*, p. 1. The scholarship on territory is vast. See here David Delaney, *Territory: A Short Introduction*, Malden, Mass.: Blackwell, 2005; Stuart Elden, *Terror and Territory: The Spatial Extent of Sovereignty*, Minneapolis: University of Minnesota Press, 2009; id., *The Birth of Territory*, Chicago and London: University of Chicago Press, 2013; Saskia Sassen, *Territory, Authority, Rights: From Medieval to Global*

Maier's approach is informed by an engagement with a range of human and political geographers, among them John Agnew and Robert Sack. In an oft-cited article from 1994, Agnew cautioned against what he called 'the territorial trap', i.e. the illusion of timeless territoriality, and the fallacies this entailed. He cast doubt on some of the 'geographical assumptions' which, at the time, were widespread in international relations (IR) theory. These included a tendency to view states as 'fixed units of sovereign space' and as 'containers of society', unaffected by the passage of time.[12] From the late 1980s and early 1990s, Agnew had also been instrumental in establishing a new subfield at the intersection of geography and IR. This came to be known as 'critical geopolitics'. It set out to dissect the hidden assumptions, motivations, and strategies behind the geographical thinking, framing and making of foreign policy. In other words, 'critical geopolitics' aimed to examine the ways in which political actors and thinkers *spatialized* world politics.[13] This comprised the debunking of 'naturalistic fallacies', such as the notion of supposedly 'natural borders' (rivers, mountain ranges etc.) or the assumption of a geopolitical 'heartland' and 'geographical pivot of history' (as outlined by British geographer Halford Mackinder in 1904).[14] It also entailed a historicization of the various founders and prominent proponents of geopolitics, from the late nineteenth century to the Cold War. Such figures include Rudolf Kjellén, Friedrich Ratzel, Alfred Thayer Mahan, Mackinder, Karl Haushofer, Carl Schmitt, Isaiah Bowman, and Yves Lacoste.[15]

*Assemblages*, Princeton: Princeton University Press, 2006; David Storey, *Territory: The Claiming of Space*, Harlow: Pearson/Prentice Hall, 2001; see also Allan Charles Dawson, Laura Zanotti and Ismael Vaccaro (eds.), *Negotiating Territoriality: Spatial Dialogues between State and Tradition*, New York: Routledge, 2014.

[12] John Agnew, 'The Territorial Trap: The Geographical Assumptions of International Relations Theory', *Review of International Political Economy* 1/1, 1994, 53–80; see also Peter J. Taylor, 'The State as Container: Territoriality in the Modern World-System', *Progress in Human Geography* 18, 1994, 151-62; see, more recently, John Agnew, *Globalization and Sovereignty: Beyond the Territorial Trap*, 2nd ed., Lanham: Rowman & Littlefield, 2018, first published 2009; Mat Coleman and John Agnew (eds.), *Handbook on the Geographies of Power*, Cheltenham: Edward Elgar, 2018.

[13] See John Agnew, 'The Origins of Critical Geopolitics', in Klaus Dodds, Merje Kuus and Joanne Sharp (eds.), *The Ashgate Research Companion to Critical Geopolitics*, Farnham: Ashgate, 2013, pp. 19-32; see also John Agnew, *Geopolitics: Re-visioning World Politics*, 2nd ed., London and New York: Routledge, 2003, first published 1998; for a foundational article see Gearóid Ó Tuathail and John Agnew, 'Geopolitics and Discourse: Practical Geopolitical Reasoning and American Foreign Policy', *Political Geography* 11, 1992, 190–204.

[14] Leslie W. Hepple, 'The Revival of Geopolitics', *Political Geography Quarterly* (Supplement) 5/4, 1986, S21–S36, here S33.

[15] See Maier, *Once within Borders*, pp. 236-76; see also Or Rosenboim, *The Emergence of Globalism: Visions of World Order in Britain and The United States, 1939-1950*, Princeton: Princeton University

One of Agnew's primary goals was the re-assertion of a 'historical-geographical consciousness' in scholarship on territory and sovereignty.[16] He had a strong ally here in geographer Robert Sack. In 1986, Sack had published a major work on the subject of 'human territoriality' as part of the series *Cambridge Studies in Historical Geography*. Even today, this text remains a key reference point. Human agency and intentionality are central to Sack's understanding of 'human territoriality'. This emerges as a deliberate strategy with potentially important effects. Sack defines it as 'the attempt by an individual or group to affect, influence, or control people, phenomena, and relationships, by delimiting and asserting control over a geographic area'. Territories are not simply 'there'. To exist, they require 'constant effort' in order to establish and maintain them. Less important than what they are, however, is what they do – they exert control over 'people and things'.[17] The purpose of human territoriality, then, is bound up with the control of behaviour. This can relate to a variety of areas, ranging from the home and the workplace to parishes, neighbourhoods, prisons and enclosures.

Another promising undertaking in this area is to be found in the work of Matthias Middell and his Leipzig-based collaborative research project, which focuses on 'processes of spatialization under the global condition'.[18] Next to Jürgen Osterhammel, Middell is perhaps foremost among those scholars who emphasise the intimate connection between 'global history and the spatial turn'. Indeed, this was the title of a programmatic article from 2010, co-authored by

---

Press, 2017. 'Critical geopolitics' has become a vast field of research, populated by some of Agnew's students, especially Gerard Toal (Gearóid Ó Tuathail), Jo Sharp, and Mathew Coleman, as well as other geographers such as Simon Dalby, Klaus Dodds, Merje Kuus and Peter Taylor. See, especially, Jason Dittmer and Joanne Sharp (eds.), *Geopolitics: An Introductory Reader*, London and New York: Routledge, 2014; Klaus Dodds, *Geopolitics: A Very Short Introduction,* 3rd ed., Oxford: Oxford University Press, 2019, first published 2007; Klaus Dodds and David Atkinson (eds.), *Geopolitical Traditions: A Century of Geopolitical Thought*, London and New York: Routledge, 2000; Dodds, Kuus and Sharp (eds.), *Ashgate Research Companion to Critical Geopolitics,* Gearóid Ó Tuathail, *Critical Geopolitics: The Politics of Writing Global Space*, London and New York: Routledge, 1996; Gearóid Ó Tuathail, Simon Dalby and Paul Routledge (eds.), *The Geopolitics Reader*, 2nd ed., London and New York: Routledge, 2006, first published 1998.

[16] Agnew, 'Territorial Trap', 77.

[17] Robert David Sack, *Human Territoriality: Its Theory and History*, Cambridge: Cambridge University Press, 1986, pp. 1, 18-9; for Sack's reflections on 'space' more generally, see id., *Conceptions of Space in Social Thought: A Geographic Perspective*, London and Basingstoke: Macmillan, 1980.

[18] See the webpage of this Collaborative Research Centre, funded by the German Research Foundation. Available HTTP: <https://research.uni-leipzig.de/~sfb1199/> (accessed 19 March 2021).

Middell and Katja Naumann. In this article, the authors advance a tripartite conceptual framework. This comprises 'regimes of territorialization' (imperial, national, multi-scalar), 'critical junctures of globalization' (crises, wars, revolutions), and 'portals of globalization' (ports, cities, and other hubs of transcultural 'glocal' encounters).[19]

More recently, this framework has been complemented by concepts of 'spatial format' and 'spatial order'. The first of these encapsulates long-lasting, wide-spread, and self-conscious formats of spatialization, such as empire, settler colony, nation-state, region, transregional organization, trade zone, and intellectual network. 'Spatial order', meanwhile, relates to a set of interdependent and relationally intertwined spatial formats. These concepts are made tangible through a focus on the perceptions, intentions and spatial practices of concrete historical actors.[20] Several studies have emerged from the Leipzig-based research centre which apply the various analytical components of 'spatial formats under the global condition' to empirical case studies. These include works on Mumbai's ports (1833-2014), the American West and South in the nineteenth century, and 'space-making and multiple territorialities' in the

---

[19] Matthias Middell and Katja Naumann, 'Global History and the Spatial Turn. From the Impact of Area Studies to the Study of Critical Junctures of Globalization', *Journal of Global History* 5, 2010, 149-70; see also Matthias Middell, 'Die konstruktivistische Wende, der *spatial turn* und das Interesse an der Globalisierung in der gegenwärtigen Geschichtswissenschaft', *Geographische Zeitschrift* 93/1, 2005, 33-44; id., 'From Universal History to Transregional Perspectives: The Challenge of the Cultural and Spatial Turn to World and Global History in the 1970s and Today', *Cultural History* 9, 2020, 241-64, here esp. 254-9; Holger Weiss (ed.), *Locating the Global: Spaces, Networks, and Interactions from the Seventeenth to the Twentieth Century*, Berlin: De Gruyter, 2020; influential here was Michael Geyer, 'Portals of Globalization', in Winfried Eberhard and Christian Lübke (eds.), *The Plurality of Europe: Identities and Spaces*, Leipzig: Leipziger Universitätsverlag, 2010, pp. 509-20; id. and Charles Bright, 'World History in a Global Age', *American Historical Review*, 100, 1995, 1034-60; for a recent major study on port cities see John Darwin, *Unlocking the World: Port Cities and Globalization in the Age of Steam, 1830-1930*, London: Allen Lane, 2020; see also in this context Christian G. De Vito, 'History without Scale: The Micro-Spatial Perspective', *Past and Present* 242, 2019, Supplement 14, 348-72; id. and Anne Gerritsen (eds.), *Micro-Spatial Histories of Global Labour*, Cham: Palgrave Macmillan, 2018.

[20] Matthias Middell, 'Category of Spatial Formats: To What End?', in Steffi Marung and Matthias Middell (eds.), *Spatial Formats under the Global Condition*, Berlin: De Gruyter, 2019, 15-47; see also id. (ed.), *The Routledge Handbook of Transregional Studies*, London and New York: Routledge, 2019. Middell also builds a historical periodization, and dialectics, into his framework, which serve to distinguish it from related but less historically oriented contributions, such as the 'territory, place, scale, network' (TPSN) approach developed by sociologists Bob Jessop and Neil Brenner and geographer Martin Jones. For the TPSN framework see Bob Jessop, Neil Brenner and Martin Jones, 'Theorizing Sociospatial Relations', *Environment and Planning D: Society and Space* 26, 2008, 389-401; Bob Jessop, 'Spatiotemporal Fixes and Multispatial Metagovernance: The Territory, Place, Scale, Network Scheme Revisited', in Marung and Middell (eds.), *Spatial Formats*, 48-77.

borderlands of nineteenth- and twentieth-century East and Central Africa.[21]

This body of scholarship represents a particular approach to the history of territoriality. A very different approach has been pursued by the historical sociologist Chandra Mukerji. Her book *Territorial Ambitions and the Gardens of Versailles* (1997) is a theoretically engaged, yet granular and finely detailed, contribution to the field. The book is replete with engravings, sketches, plans, and photographs. It convincingly relates territoriality to material culture and the built environment. The central focus lies on Louis XIV's famous gardens. These emerge as 'expressions of a new French political territoriality' that evolved during the seventeenth century. Mukerji shows how the earthworks of Versailles served as tools and laboratories of power. They both reflected and demonstrated transformations in the governance and territoriality of France itself. Mukerji is a ceaseless drawer of lines and connections. She undertakes this partly through analogy, and partly by making causal links. Her connections traverse, on the one hand, Versailles's walls, moats, and canals, the landscape grading and terraces for surveying the land, and, on other, Sébastien de Vauban's fortress designs and other features of French military engineering. Territoriality is approached here through the 'material manipulation of the land'. As Mukerji emphatically states, the France which emerges from the book is very much 'a place'.[22]

A multifaceted complication of the idea of territory is one of the many benefits of *An Aqueous Territory* (2016), Ernesto Bassi's study of the 'transimperial Greater Caribbean' in the late eighteenth and early nineteenth centuries. The book is based on a thorough engagement with spatial theory –

21 See Megan Maruschke, *Portals of Globalization: Repositioning Mumbai's Ports and Zones, 1833–2014*, Berlin: De Gruyter, 2019; Steffen Wöll, *The West and the Word: Imagining, Formatting, and Ordering the American West in Nineteenth-Century Cultural Discourse*, Berlin: De Gruyter, 2020; Deniz Bozkurt-Pekár, *Imagining Southern Spaces: Hemispheric and Transatlantic Souths in Antebellum US Writings*, Berlin: De Gruyter, 2021; Geert Castryck (ed.), Special Issue on 'The Bounds of Berlin's Africa: Space-Making and Multiple Territorialities in East and Central Africa', *International Journal of African Historical Studies* 52/1, 2019; see also Gabriele Pisarz-Ramirez and Hannes Warnecke-Berger (eds.), *Processes of Spatialization in the Americas: Configurations and Narratives*, Bern: Peter Lang, 2018; for a full list of publications from the series *Dialectics of the Global* see the publisher's webpage. Available HTTP: <https://www.degruyter.com/serial/DIGLO-B/html> (accessed 19 March 2021).

22 Chandra Mukerji, *Territorial Ambitions and the Gardens of Versailles*, Cambridge: Cambridge University Press, 1997, pp. 18, 309, 324; see also id., 'Dominion, Demonstration, and Domination: Religious Doctrine, Territorial Politics, and French Plant Collection', in Londa Schiebinger and Claudia Swan (ed.), *Colonial Botany: Science, Commerce, and Politics in the Early Modern World*, Philadelphia: University of Pennsylvania Press, 2005, pp. 19-33, id., 'The Archives Made Me Do It', *Qualitative Sociology* 43, 2020, 305-16.

names such as Agnew, Lefebvre and Massey all feature. Bassi refuses to follow in the footsteps of nation- and empire-centred historiography. Instead, he charts the routes of sailors criss-crossing political borders and creating their own 'transimperial' region of 'islands, continental coasts, and open waters' along the way. Such 'everyday acts of region making' often eschewed territorial control. The sailors navigated with relative ease between various ports. They came to inhabit and produce 'a space that was [...] *simultaneously* Spanish, British, and French, as well as Dutch, Danish, Anglo-American, African'. At the same time, Bassi acknowledges that political borders in the early nineteenth century did increasingly thwart 'geopolitical imaginations' of a 'transimperial' Caribbean. A striking example here is Colombia's formation as a self-consciously Andean-*Atlantic* nation.[23]

The history of territoriality is intimately linked to the history of infrastructure. Railroads, telegraphs, bridges – these have a decisive impact on time and space.[24] It is unsurprising that Chandra Mukerji, with her abiding interest in both materiality and territoriality, has turned to the subject of infrastructure in her more recent work. Her book *Impossible Engineering* (2009), for example, focuses on the late-seventeenth-century construction of the Canal du Midi, which connected the Atlantic with the Mediterranean.[25] Mukerji sees infrastructure as a material form of 'impersonal rule'. To be sure, it can lend

---

[23] Ernesto Bassi, *An Aqueous Territory: Sailor Geography and new Granada's Transimperial Greater Caribbean World*, Durham: Duke University Press, 2016, pp. 9, 81 (own emphasis); for a further example of how to apply the notion of territoriality to maritime history see Michael Talbot's chapter in Bavaj, Lawson and Struck (eds.), *Doing Spatial History*.

[24] It is little wonder that infrastructure features so prominently in Charles Maier's *Once within Borders*, pp. 188-214; on railroads, see the classic works by Wolfgang Schivelbusch, *The Railway Journey*, Berkeley: University of California Press, 1986, German 1977, ch. 3 ('Railroad Space and Railroad Time'); and Richard White, *Railroaded: The Transcontinentals and the Making of Modern America*, New York: W.W. Norton, 2011; as well as Zef M. Segal, *The Political Fragmentation of Germany: Formation of German States by Infrastructures, Maps, and Movement, 1815-1866*, Cham: Palgrave Macmillan, 2019; and Benjamin Schenk's chapter in Bavaj, Lawson and Struck (eds.), *Doing Spatial History*; on telegraphs, see especially Todd A. Diacon, *Stringing Together a Nation: Cândido Mariano da Silva Rondon and the Construction of a Modern Brazil 1906-1930*, Durham: Duke University Press, 2004; Michael Mann, *Wiring the Nation: Telecommunication, Newspaper-Reportage, and Nation Building in British India 1850-1930*, Oxford: Oxford University Press, 2017; Simone M. Müller, *Wiring the World: The Social and Cultural Creation of Global Telegraph Networks*, New York: Columbia University Press, 2016; Heidi J.S. Tworek, *News from Germany: The Competition to Control World Communications,1900-1945*, Cambridge, Mass.: Harvard University Press, 2019; on highway construction in eighteenth- and early-nineteenth-century Britain's 'infrastructure state', see Jo Guldi, *Roads to Power: Britain Invents the Infrastructure State*, Cambridge, Mass.: Harvard University Press, 2012.

[25] Chandra Mukerji, *Impossible Engineering: Technology and Territoriality on the Canal du Midi*, Princeton: Princeton University Press, 2009.

states a 'palpable presence'. And yet it often works 'below the level of conscious awareness'. Moreover, rather than necessarily acting as an enabling force for political elites, it may also, over time, restrict their room for manoeuvre – in some cases, quite severely.[26]

This observation serves to complicate the view of state power as laid out by the classic *Seeing Like A State* (1998). In this book, political scientist and anthropologist James C. Scott makes the case for a more clear-cut link between, on the one hand, the power of ruling elites and, on the other, material constructions. These may include infrastructural projects that emerge from centralized state planning and are rooted in a 'high modernist' zeal to 'improve the human condition'.[27]

Historian Dirk van Laak, a key figure in this field, has described infrastructures as 'material links between the past, present and future of a society'.[28] They transcend political ruptures and constitute long-term path dependencies. Typically, they are defined as means of supply and disposal (of water, waste and so on), and of transport and communication. In most cases, they are materially tangible. Moreover, they are key components of daily routines. They, therefore, appear timeless and ever-present – a 'background technology' that tends to be innocuous, provided that it 'works'.

---

[26] Mukerji, *Impossible Engineering*, pp. 203-27; Patrick Joyce and Chandra Mukerji, 'The State of Things: State History and Theory Reconfigured', *Theory and Society* 46, 2017, 1-19, here 2-3; see also Chandra Mukerji, 'The Territorial State as a Figured World of Power: Strategies, Logistics and Impersonal Rule', *Sociological Theory* 28, 2010, 402-24.

[27] James C. Scott, *Seeing Like a State: How Certain Schemes to Improve the Human Condition Have Failed*, New Haven: Yale University Press, 1998, p. 88.

[28] Dirk van Laak, 'Infrastrukturen', *Docupedia-Zeitgeschichte*, 1.12.2020. Available HTTP: <http://docupedia.de/zg/Laak_infrastrukturen_v1_de_2020> (accessed 19 March 2021) (with an extensive reference section). The description offered here closely follows van Laak's immensely helpful introduction to the history of infrastructure. See also Dirk van Laak, 'Garanten der Beständigkeit', in Anselm Doering-Manteuffel (ed.), *Strukturmerkmale der deutschen Geschichte des 20. Jahrhunderts*, Munich: Oldenbourg, 2006, pp. 167-80; for English-speaking overviews and case study collections see Nikhil Anand, Akhil Gupta and Hannah Appel (eds.), *The Promise of Infrastructure*, Durham: Duke University Press, 2018; Maria Paula Diogo and Dirk van Laak, *Europeans Globalizing: Mapping, Exploiting, Exchanging*, London: Palgrave Macmillan, 2016; Penelope Harvey, Casper Bruun Jensen and Atsuro Morita (eds.), *Infrastructures and Social Complexity: A Companion*, London: Palgrave Macmillan, 2017; Per Högselius, Arne Kaijser and Erik van der Vleuten, *Europe's Infrastructure Transition: Economy, War, Nature*, London: Palgrave Macmillan, 2015; Erik van der Vleuten and Arne Kaijser (eds.), *Networking Europe: Transnational Infrastructures and the Shaping of Europe, 1850-2000*, Sagamore Beach, Mass.: Science History Publications, 2006; see also Christian Henrich-Franke, 'Historical Infrastructure Research: A (Sub-)Discipline in the Making?', in Matthias Korn et al. (eds.), *Infrastructuring Publics*, Wiesbaden: Springer, 2019, pp. 49-68.

Infrastructures provide fixed, material structures that facilitate *flows*: of resources, goods, and information. Indeed, the title of van Laak's major work on the subject is: 'Everything in flux'.[29] Infrastructures are a hallmark of modern society, and of the acceleration of modern life. Typically, they are made for 'anonymous use', and for participation in the 'common good'. Consequently, they have been seen as an important means of integration. They serve to unlock and connect territories – economically, socially, and culturally. They function as a key strategy in the creation of simultaneity and 'spatial uniformity', exerting a conditioning and disciplining effect on behaviour. For all of these reasons, infrastructures have played a crucial role in processes of nation-building. Clearly, however, access to infrastructure tends to vary along social, ethnic and geographic lines – between, for example, city and countryside. As in other areas of social life, processes of inclusion and exclusion are inextricably linked. Importantly, moreover, the political intent and in-built technological tendency to homogenize space is frequently countered by culturally specific appropriations of infrastructure.[30]

The spatial-historical implications of infrastructural projects have been illuminated by a range of studies that have appeared over the past twenty to thirty years. In *Connecting the Nineteenth-Century World* (2013), for example, global historian Roland Wenzlhuemer offers a detailed analysis of the expanding submarine telegraph network in the late nineteenth century. He shows the pivotal role of Britain and British India in shaping these networks. To be sure, it is not entirely surprising that London is highlighted as a global communication hub, with considerable regional unevenness of connectivity. Methodologically, however, Wenzlhuemer's focus on both network structure and network use are highly instructive. So too is his map-, chart-, and cartoon-based combination of quantitative and qualitative analysis. Moreover, his book is closely informed by spatial theory. Wenzlhuemer is thus able to adeptly distinguish between a variety of relationally conceived spaces (communication space, transport space, telephone cost space, transport cost space). He critically engages with contemporary notions of the 'annihilation of space through time'. In place of this concept, Wenzlhuemer suggests that telegraph-driven globalization be framed in terms of a 'detachment of patterns of human communication from geographic proximity'. New spaces were produced, and

[29] Dirk van Laak, *Alles im Fluss: Die Lebensadern unserer Gesellschaft – Geschichte und Zukunft der Infrastruktur*, Frankfurt/Main: S. Fischer, 2018.
[30] Van Laak, 'Infrastrukturen'.

others transformed. Above all, 'communication space' condensed along an infrastructural axis between North America's East Coast, London, Europe, and South Asia.[31]

The entanglement of global infrastructures and regional environments is at the heart of *Beyond the Big Ditch* (2014), Ashley Carse's interdisciplinary study on the Panama Canal watershed. Carse, a cultural anthropologist, bases his study on detailed archival research, ethnographic fieldwork and interviews, as well as a thorough command of spatial theory. His book demonstrates that the 1914 opening of the famous waterway marked the beginning of an 'ongoing social and environmental management project'.[32] Certainly, infrastructures are typically created to alleviate some of the inconveniences of daily life. And yet their maintenance can be highly demanding. To paraphrase the late sociologist Susan Leigh Star: 'One person's infrastructure is another's problem'.[33]

This is amply demonstrated by the case of the Panama Canal. Enormous amounts of fresh water were needed per transit of ship, while the 1970s and 1980s saw rising anxieties about an apparently impending water shortage. This resulted in a burgeoning competition over the surrounding forest between interoceanic transportation and slash-and-burn agriculture. What this actually entailed was a conflict between canal administrators and smallholder farmers (*campesino*), while both groups were themselves integrated into global infrastructures and territorial politics. Ultimately, canal-related 'scale-making projects' certainly created new connections between oceans. However, they also produced *disconnections* between people and places.[34]

Another illuminating example here is provided by Julia Tischler's *Light and Power for a Multiracial Nation* (2013), which focuses on the construction of the

[31] Roland Wenzlhuemer, *Connecting the Nineteenth-Century World: The Telegraph and Globalization*, Cambridge: Cambridge University Press, 2013, pp. 15, 37-50, 253-7; id., 'Globalization, Communication and the Concept of Space in Global History', *Historical Social Research* 35/1, 2010, 19-47, here esp. 27; see also id., *Doing Global History: An Introduction in 6 Concepts*, London: Bloomsbury, 2020, German 2017, ch. 3 ('Space: Connectivity and Isolation'); as well as Osterhammel, *Transformation of the World*.

[32] Ashley Carse, *Beyond the Big Ditch: Politics, Ecology, and Infrastructure at the Panama Canal*, Cambridge, Mass.: MIT Press, 2014; id., 'Response', *H-Environment Roundtable Reviews* 5/10, 2015, 18-29, here 20.

[33] Susan Leigh Star, 'The Ethnography of Infrastructure', *American Behavioral Scientist* 43, 1999, 377-91, here 380. The paraphrase is borrowed from Carse, 'Response', 23.

[34] Carse, 'Response', 23; see also the comments by Chandra Mukerji, *H-Environment Roundtable Reviews* 5/10, 2015, 11-12; for a recent study on the Suez canal see Valeska Huber, *Channelling Mobilities: Migration and Globalisation in the Suez Canal Region and Beyond, 1869–1914*, Cambridge: Cambridge University Press, 2013.

Kariba Dam in the latter half of the 1950s. The creation of this hydroelectric dam on the border between today's Zambia and Zimbabwe entailed the eviction and resettlement of 57,000 Gwembe Tonga peasants from their Zambezi riverine villages. As Tischler shows, it also served to 'cement' patterns of 'uneven development' in racial as well as rural/urban relations. The legacy of this infrastructural project – and its impact – was to endure throughout the postcolonial period.[35]

Indeed, much scholarship has focused on the relationship between water infrastructure and urban modernity. Cultural geographer Matthew Gandy's study *The Fabric of Space* (2014), for example, takes the reader on a journey from nineteenth-century Paris to postcolonial Lagos and contemporary Mumbai.[36] Needless to say, infrastructure has also become a subject for social historians. Ravi Ahuja's *Pathways of Empire* (2009) and Aparajita Mukhopadhyay's *Imperial Technology and 'Native' Agency* (2018) are two notable works of spatially informed history writing that focus on infrastructure. These contributions examine roads, canals, and railways in colonial India as 'materializations of social relations in space', which served to foreground questions of access and social transformation.[37]

Both the history of territoriality and the history of infrastructure are closely related to the history of borders. As mentioned, Charles Maier's *Once within Borders* essentially diagnoses a transition from 'fuzzy' frontier zones to clear

---

[35] Julia Tischler, *Light and Power for a Multiracial Nation: The Kariba Dam Scheme in the Central African Federation*, Basingstoke: Palgrave Macmillan, 2013; id., 'Cementing Uneven Development: The Central African Federation and the Kariba Dam Scheme', *Journal of Southern African Studies* 40, 2014, 1047-64; see also Jonas van der Straeten and Ute Hasenöhrl, 'Connecting the Empire: New Research Perspectives on Infrastructures and the Environment in the (Post)Colonial World', *NTM Journal of the History of Science, Technology and Medicine* 24, 2016, 355-91.

[36] Matthew Gandy, *The Fabric of Space: Water, Modernity, and Urban Imagination*, Cambridge, Mass.: Harvard University Press, 2014; on Los Angeles, also covered by Gandy, see most recently Jan Hansen, 'Water Infrastructure and Practical Knowledge in Progressive-Era Los Angeles', *Southern California Quarterly* 102, 2020, 385-419; on urban infrastructure and media technologies, see the important study by Brian Larkin, *Signal and Noise: Media, Infrastructure, and Urban Culture in Nigeria*, Durham: Duke University Press, 2008; more generally, see Stephen Graham and Colin McFarlane (eds.), *Infrastructural Lives: Urban Infrastructure in Context*, London: Routledge, 2015; for further infrastructure-related work on cities see the section below on 'City and Home'.

[37] Ravi Ahuja, *Pathways of Empire: Circulation, 'Public Works' and Social Space in Colonial Orissa (c.1780-1914)*, Hyderabad: Orient BlackSwan, 2009, p. 9; Aparajita Mukhopadhyay, *Imperial Technology and 'Native' Agency: A Social History of Railways in Colonial India, 1850-1920*, London: Routledge, 2018; see more generally David Lambert and Peter Merriman (eds.), *Empire and Mobility in the Long Nineteenth Century*, Manchester: Manchester University Press, 2020; for German Southwest Africa, see Julio Decker, 'Lines in the Sand: Railways and the Archipelago of Colonial Territorialization in German Southwest Africa, 1897-1914', *Journal of Historical Geography* 70, 2020, 74-87.

border lines.[38] For the reasons outlined above, historical research on borders and borderlands has gathered pace since the end of the Cold War. It has frequently been rooted in 'the spatial turn'. To be sure, borders have long been the subject of historical investigation, often focussing on political hotspots such as the Mexico-United States border, the India-Pakistan border, and the borders of Israel. Indeed, the Association for Borderlands Studies, housed by Arizona State University, was founded as early as 1976. Its initial focus lay on the US-Mexican borderlands. Since 1986, this Association has been home to the *Journal of Borderlands Studies*, the flagship publication in the field. In much the same way, the Centre for Borders Research at Durham, founded in 1989 as International Boundaries Research Unit (IBRU), also preceded the end of the Cold War.[39]

Likewise, it is certainly true that the landmark study by Peter Sahlins on the Franco-Spanish border, laconically titled *Boundaries* (1989), did not originate from the political context of the fall of the Berlin Wall. Rather, it followed more directly in the wake of the 1980s cultural turn. This was evident from the book's intensive questioning of the supposed naturalness of geographical categories. Tellingly, 'Natural Frontiers Revisited' was the title of an article derived from Sahlins' book and published in the *American Historical Review*. In this article, he argued that borders are anything but natural. Sahlins partly drew inspiration from Gaston Zeller's work on France's eastern frontier and Lucien Febvre's famous study of the Rhine (both published in the 1920s and 1930s). Sahlins demonstrated that, in many respects, the 1659 Treaty of the Pyrenees was only the beginning of a long-term process of border-making. At first, the political border bore little relevance to people living on either side of it, but increasing territorial and infrastructural power rendered this border a reality. What proved decisive was the enactment of the border by local populations on the ground. To be sure, state territory was the product of central governance from the capitals of Paris and Madrid. In crucial ways, however, it was also made at the margins, in the borderlands themselves.[40]

---

[38] Maier, *Once within Borders*, pp. 33, 40, 71.

[39] IBRU's first conference was held from 14 to 17 September 1989.

[40] Peter Sahlins, *Boundaries: The Making of France and Spain in the Pyrenees*, Berkeley: University of California Press, 1989; id., 'Natural Frontiers Revisited: France's Boundaries since the Seventeenth Century', *American Historical Review* 95, 1990, 1423-51; for the expansion of road and railway networks in the late nineteenth century, see the classic study by Eugen Weber, *Peasants into Frenchmen: The Modernization of Rural France, 1870-1914*, Stanford: Stanford University Press, 1976.

Despite the existence of this scholarship, however, it was not until the 1990s that border studies became a booming field.[41] Since then, a range of centres and research networks have been formed. Notable examples include the Centre for Cross Border Studies at Armagh and Dublin (1999), and the Centre for International Borders Research at Belfast (2000), both founded in the wake of the Good Friday Agreement of 1998; the Nijmegen Centre for Border Research (1998); the Environment and Governance Research Group at the University of New South Wales, home to the journal *Borderlands* (2001); the Asian Borderlands Research Network (2008); the Eurasia Unit for Border Research, Japan (2013); and the African Borderlands Research Network (2007).

Over the past twenty years, borders and borderlands have been a prominent component of a 'spatial turn' in African studies. This can be seen from volumes such as *The Spatial Factor in African History* (2005), *Respacing Africa* (2010), and *Spatial Practices: Territory, Border and Infrastructure in Africa* (2018).[42] Paul Nugent, Professor of Comparative African History and founder of the African Borderlands Research Network, has been particularly active here.[43] His latest book *Boundaries, Communities and State-Making in West Africa* (2019) compares the borderlands of Ghana/Togo and The Gambia/Senegal. It elucidates the ways in which these states were shaped through myriad processes and policies relating to their borders. These included the conversion of pre-colonial 'frontier zones into colonial borders', as well as the regulation of 'border spaces', not least the 'border flows' of people and goods.

---

[41] For helpful overviews see Thomas M. Wilson and Hastings Donnan (eds.), *A Companion to Border Studies*, Malden, Mass.: Wiley-Blackwell, 2012; Doris Wastl-Walter (ed.), *The Ashgate Research Companion to Border Studies*, London and New York: Routledge, 2012; see also Alexander C. Diener and Joshua Hagen, *Borders: A Very Short Introduction*, Oxford: Oxford University Press, 2012; id. (eds.), *Borderlines and Borderlands: Political Oddities at the Edge of the Nation-State*, Lanham: Rowman & Littlefield, 2010; Henk van Houtum, Olivier Kramsch and Wolfgang Zierhofer (eds.), *B/ordering Space*, Aldershot: Ashgate, 2005; Günther Lottes, 'Frontiers between Geography and History', in Steven G. Ellis and Raingard Eßer (eds.), *Frontiers and the Writing of History, 1500–1850*, Hanover: Wehrhahn, 2006, pp. 39–71.

[42] Ulf Engel, Marc Boeckler and Detlev Müller-Mahn (eds.), *Spatial Practices: Territory, Border and Infrastructure in Africa*, Leiden: Brill, 2018; Ulf Engel and Paul Nugent (eds.), *Respacing Africa*, Leiden: Brill, 2010 (see especially the introduction: 'The Spatial Turn in African Studies', pp. 1-9); Allen M. Howard and Richard M. Shain (eds.), *The Spatial Factor in African History*, Leiden: Brill, 2005; see also the instructive case study by Julie MacArthur, 'Decolonizing Sovereignty: States of Exception along the Kenya-Somali Frontier', *American Historical Review* 124, 2019, 108-43.

[43] See, for instance, the useful overview chapters by Paul Nugent, 'Border Towns and Cities in Comparative Perspective', in Wilson and Donnan (eds.), *Companion to Border Studies*, 557-72; id., 'Border Studies: Temporality, Space, and Scale', in Middell (eds.), *Routledge Handbook of Transregional Studies*, 179-87.

The key message of Nugent's book is that margins are central. So too are cross-border 'realities of everyday connectivity'.[44] Indeed, Nugent already explored some of these ideas in his earlier study *Smugglers, Secessionists and Loyal Citizens on the Ghana-Togo Frontier* (2002). In this book, Nugent placed much emphasis on the agency of local populations in co-producing a border that both divided and connected them. They did so by harnessing state power (and its limits) to their advantage, and via networks of smuggling that transformed the border zone into a 'theatre of opportunity'.[45] More recently, Nugent has turned his attention to the subject of border infrastructures such as seaports and 'transport corridors'. These serve to connect urban markets and mining centres in Africa both regionally and globally.[46]

In terms of conceptual and analytical framework, scholars of borders and borderlands can draw on a pool of ideas, both old and new. Annales historian Lucien Febvre, for instance, aptly highlighted the dual function of borders as oscillating between a 'suturing' frontier zone (*couture*) and a 'severing' border line (*coupure*).[47] As the studies by Sahlins, Nugent and others have shown, the manifestations of a border often hinge on social practices on the ground – the 'lived border', as some historians have styled it.[48] This view is usually informed by a central insight formulated by sociologist Georg Simmel in 1908. Simmel suggested that 'the boundary is not a spatial fact with sociological consequences, but a sociological fact that forms itself spatially'.[49] Of varying influence have

---

[44] Paul Nugent, *Boundaries, Communities and State-Making in West Africa: The Centrality of the Margins*, Cambridge: Cambridge University Press, 2019, pp. 3-4.

[45] Paul Nugent, *Smugglers, Secessionists and Loyal Citizens on the Ghana-Togo Frontier: The Lie of the Borderlands Since 1914*, Athens: Ohio University Press, 2002, p. 273; see also id. and A.I. Asiwaju (eds.), *African Boundaries: Barriers, Conduits and Opportunities*, London and New York: Pinter, 1996.

[46] See Paul Nugent, 'Africa's Re-Enchantment with Big Infrastructure: White Elephants Dancing in Virtuous Circles?', in Jon Schubert, Ulf Engel and Elísio Macamo (eds.), *Extractive Industries and Changing State Dynamics in Africa: Beyond the Resource Curse*, London and New York: Routledge, 2018, pp. 22-40; id. and Isabella Soi, 'One-Stop Border Posts in East Africa: State Encounters of the Fourth Kind', *Journal of Eastern African Studies* 14, 2020, 433-54.

[47] Albert Demangeon and Lucien Febvre, *Le Rhin: Problèmes d'histoire et d'économie*, Paris: Colin, 1935, pp. 16-17, 72, 170; see also Claude Courlet, 'La frontière: Couture ou coupure?', *Économie et Humanisme* 301, 1988, 5-12; 'Entretien avec Thomas Serrier: Europa – Notre Histoire', *Revue Abibac*, 27 November 2019. Available HTTP: <https://revue-abibac.fr/2019/11/27/entretien-avec-thomas-serrier-europa-notre-histoire/> (accessed 19 March 2021).

[48] Etienne François, Jörg Seifarth and Bernhard Struck, 'Einleitung: Grenzen und Grenzräume. Erfahrungen und Konstruktionen', in id. (eds.), *Grenzen: Räume, Erfahrungen, Konstruktionen, 17.-20. Jahrhundert*, Frankfurt/Main and New York: Campus, 2006, pp. 7-29, here p. 21.

[49] Georg Simmel, 'The Sociology of Space', 1908, in David Frisby and Mike Featherstone (eds.), *Simmel on Culture: Selected Writings*, London: Sage, 1997, p. 142.

been typologies of borderlands from 'infant' to 'defunct', from 'alienated' to 'integrated', and from 'quiet' to 'rebellious'.[50] Philosophical and anthropological conceptualizations of borders have also played a role here.[51] A widely-cited example comprises Gloria Anzaldúa's semi-autobiographical reflections on the US-Mexican borderlands. She characterises these as indicative of psychological, linguistic, sexual and gender identity dynamics that are fundamental to 'border cultures' more generally.[52]

Both thematically and geographically, historical research on borders and borderlands has been impressively wide-ranging. Its scope can only be highlighted here in the briefest possible way. Standout works include D. Graham Burnett's *Masters of All They Surveyed* (2000). This book was partly inspired by Paul Carter's 'spatial history', as well as by Greg Dening's *Islands and Beaches* (1980). Burnett incisively dissects colonial practices of 'traverse' or route surveying, landmark creation, and boundary making in nineteenth-century British Guiana in South America.[53] Another key study which dovetails nicely with Burnett's book, and which focuses on the same period, is Thomas Simpson's theoretically-attuned *The Frontier in British India* (2021). This work elucidates how frontiers in northwest and northeast India turned out to be fluctuating, uncontrollable, '"messy" spaces', which served to embody the 'limits of the colonial state' in more than one respect.[54] Tamar Herzog's

---

[50] Michiel Baud and Willem van Schendel, 'Toward a Comparative History of Borderlands', *Journal of World History* 8, 1997, 211-42; Oscar J. Martínez, *Border People: Life and Society in the U.S.-Mexico Borderlands*, Tucson: University of Arizona Press, 1994; Eric Tagliacozzo, 'Jagged Landscapes: Conceptualizing Borders and Boundaries in the History of Human Societies', *Journal of Borderlands Studies* 31, 2016, 1-21.

[51] See Edward S. Casey, *The World on Edge*, Bloomington: Indiana University Press, 2017, esp. pp. 7-27; id., 'Border versus Boundary at La Frontera', *Environment and Planning D: Society and Space* 29, 2011, 384-98; id. and Mary Watkins, *Up Against the Wall: Re-Imagining the U.S.-Mexico Border*, University of Texas Press, 2014; Hastings Donnan and Thomas M. Wilson, *Borders: Frontiers of Identity, Nation and State*, Oxford and New York: Berg, 1999; Thomas M. Wilson and Hastings Donnan (eds.), *Border Identities: Nation and State at International Frontiers*, Cambridge: Cambridge University Press, 1998; see also Alexander C. Diener and Joshua Hagen, 'The Political Sociology and Political Geography of Borders', in William Outhwaite and Stephen P. Turner (eds.), *The Sage Handbook of Political Sociology*, Los Angeles: Sage, 2017, 330-46; Martina Löw and Gunter Weidenhaus, 'Borders that Relate: Conceptualizing Boundaries in Relational Space', *Current Sociology Monograph* 65, 2017, 553-70; Sandro Mezzadra and Brett Neilson, *Border as Method, or, the Multiplication of Labor*, Durham: Duke University Press, 2013.

[52] Gloria Anzaldúa, *Borderlands/La Frontera: The New Mestiza*, San Francisco: Spinsters/Aunt Lute, 1987.

[53] D. Graham Burnett, *Masters of All They Surveyed: Exploration, Geography, and a British El Dorado*, Chicago and London: University of Chicago Press, 2000.

[54] Thomas Simpson, *The Frontier in British India: Space, Science, and Power in the Nineteenth Century*,

*Frontiers of Possession* (2015), meanwhile, draws on a legal history perspective to show how boundaries between early modern Portugal and Spain were formed on both sides of the Atlantic. This book throws into sharp relief the relationship between, on the one hand, treaty making and border legislation and, on the other, common legal cultures and conflicting local interests. These ranged from settlers to soldiers, who fiercely contested their right to land.[55]

International law and the multiple dimensions of 'the local' are also part of Nianshen Song's *Making Borders in Modern East Asia* (2018). This book focuses on turn-of-the-century disputes over the China-Korea border. In particular, it explores the Tumen River borderlands as an 'integrated socioecological unit' constituted by Chinese, Korean, Japanese and Russian power rivalries, state-building competition, socio-economic cross-border interactions, and the formation of a Korean diaspora in Northeast China.[56] Alyssa Park's *Sovereignty Experiments* (2019) is complementary to Song's study. Park analyses processes of territorialization in Northeast Asia from the vantage point of Korean migration, as well as persistent attempts to control it by Korean, Chinese, Japanese, and Russian authorities. This ultimately lead to the creation of the strict border regime that still exists between Russia, China, and North Korea.[57]

Indeed, Asian borderlands have been the subject of much research over the past two decades. This has ranged from work on Qing China's Yunnan frontier to investigations of smuggling in modern Southeast Asia, and studies on Iranian nation-building.[58] Needless to say, borderlands in other parts of the world thus

---

Cambridge: Cambridge University Press, 2021, pp. 7, 67.

[55] Tamar Herzog, *Frontiers of Possession: Spain and Portugal in Europe and the Americas*, Cambridge, Mass.: Harvard University Press, 2015; see also Lauren Benton, *A Search for Sovereignty: Law and Geography in European Empires, 1400–1900*, Cambridge: Cambridge University Press, 2010; Jeffrey Alan Erbig Jr., *Where Caciques and Mapmakers Met: Border Making in Eighteenth-Century South America*, Chapel Hill: University of North Carolina Press, 2020.

[56] Nianshen Song, *Making Borders in Modern East Asia: The Tumen River Demarcation, 1881-1919*, Cambridge: Cambridge University Press, 2018, p. 10; see also id., 'A Buffer against Whom? Rethinking the Qing-Chosŏn Border Region', *Geopolitics*, published online: 21 Dec 2020. Available HTTP: <https://doi.org/10.1080/14650045.2020.1844670> (accessed 19 March 2021).

[57] Alyssa M. Park, *Sovereignty Experiments: Korean Migrants and the Building of Borders in Northeast Asia, 1860–1945*, Ithaca: Cornell University Press, 2019.

[58] See C. Patterson Giersch, *Asian Borderlands: The Transformation of Qing China's Yunnan Frontier*, Cambridge, Mass.: Harvard University Press, 2006; Firoozeh Kashani-Sabet, *Frontier Fictions: Shaping the Iranian Nation, 1804-1946*, London: I.B. Tauris, 1999; Eric Tagliacozzo, *Secret Trade, Porous Borders: Smuggling and States along a Southeast Asian Frontier, 1865-1915*, New Haven: Yale University Press, 2005; see also Peter C. Perdue, 'Crossing Borders in Imperial China', in Eric Tagliacozzo, Helen F. Siu, Peter C. Perdue (eds.), *Asia Inside Out: Connected Places*, Cambridge, Mass.: Harvard University Press, 2015, 195-218; id., 'Boundaries, Maps, and Movement: Chinese,

far unmentioned in this section have drawn increased scholarly attention as well. Recent work on Central Europe, for instance, has taken in language frontiers in the Habsburg Empire; borders and the movement of goods and people in the Holy Roman Empire; borderland schooling in interwar Europe; and the Cold-War inner German border of the Iron Curtain.[59]

## Territories, Boundaries and Consciousness

How can we analytically approach the many ways in which boundaries, across various scales, are both socially produced and themselves agents of identity formation? An answer to this question can be gleaned from the model study on the Finnish-Russian border by political geographer Anssi Paasi.[60] This contribution draws widely on spatial theory. It touches on Lefebvre, Foucault, Giddens, Sack, Agnew, Massey, and Peter Taylor, and deploys spatial theory to great effect in empirical analysis.[61] The book traces the 'changing geographies'

---

Russian, and Mongolian Empires in Early Modern Central Eurasia', *The International History Review* 20, 1998, 263-86; as well as the chapter by Lisa Hellman in Bavaj, Lawson and Struck (eds.), *Doing Spatial History*.

[59] See Pieter M. Judson, *Guardians of the Nation: Activists on the Language Frontiers of Imperial Austria*, Cambridge, Mass.: Harvard University Press, 2006; Andreas Rutz, *Die Beschreibung des Raums: Territoriale Grenzziehungen im Heiligen Römischen Reich*, Cologne: Böhlau, 2018; Luca Scholz, *Borders & Freedom of Movement in the Holy Roman Empire*, Oxford: Oxford University Press, 2020; Machteld Venken, *Peripheries at the Centre: Borderland Schooling in Interwar Europe*, New York: Berghahn 2021; David H. Kaplan and Jouni Häkli (eds.), *Boundaries and Place: European Borderlands in Geographical Context*, Lanham: Rowman & Littlefield, 2002; Edith Sheffer, *Burned Bridge: How East and West Germans Made the Iron Curtain*, Oxford: Oxford University Press, 2011; Sagi Schaefer, *States of Division: Border and Boundary Formation in Cold War Rural Germany*, Oxford: Oxford University Press, 2014; Jason B. Johnson, *Divided Village: The Cold War in the German Borderlands*, London and New York: Routledge, 2017; Astrid Eckert, *West Germany and the Iron Curtain: Environment, Economy, and Culture in the Borderlands*, Oxford: Oxford University Press, 2019; see also the review article by Andrew S. Tompkins, 'Binding the Nation, Bounding the State: Germany and Its Borders', *German History* 37, 2019, 77-100. A global scope offers the stimulating volume by Paul Readman, Cynthia Radding and Chad Bryant (eds.), *Borderlands in World History, 1700-1914*, Basingstoke: Palgrave Macmillan, 2014.

[60] Anssi Paasi, *Territories, Boundaries and Consciousness: The Changing Geographies of the Finnish-Russian Border*, New York: J. Wiley & Sons, 1996; id., 'Boundaries as Social Practice and Discourse: The Finnish-Russian Border', *Regional Studies* 33, 1999, 669-80, here esp. 676; see also, more generally, id., 'Place and Region: Regional Worlds and Words', *Progress in Human Geography* 26, 2002, 802-11; id., 'Region and Place: Regional Identity in Question', *Progress in Human Geography* 27, 2003, 475-85; id., 'Place and Region: Looking Through the Prism of Scale', *Progress in Human Geography* 28, 2004, 536-46; id., 'Border Studies Reanimated: Going Beyond the Territorial/Relational Divide', *Environment and Planning A* 44, 2012, 2303-9; id., John Harrison and Martin Jones (eds.), *Handbook on the Geographies of Regions and Territories*, Cheltenham: Edward Elgar, 2018.

[61] See, especially, Peter J. Taylor, *Political Geography: World-Economy, Nation-State and Locality*, 3rd ed., New York: J. Wiley & Sons, 1993, first published 1985; id., 'The State as Container'.

of Finland's eastern border during the twentieth century, with a focal point on critical junctures of the 1940s, the Cold War period, and its aftermath.

In 1917, Finland separated from Russia and gained independence. The eastern border thereupon attained great significance within the state-driven project of Finnish nation-building. Both within this context and on a broader international plane, the border also acquired meanings of a symbolic boundary 'between two worlds'. These worlds appeared as politically, ideologically, and religiously distinct from each other. On the eastern side of the border lay a dictatorial, communist 'East' with uncanny continuities of Byzantine Orthodoxy. The western side, meanwhile, was the site of a democratic, capitalist 'West', strongly rooted in Lutheran Protestantism.

Certainly, Finland remained 'neutral' and subject to Soviet influence ('Finlandization') throughout the Cold War. To this day, Finland has not joined NATO. And yet the border to Russia could be used by the Finnish state to promote an 'us' / 'them' rhetoric and to foster a sense of national belonging. This strategy could also harness the dire legacy of territorial losses and economic weakening inflicted on Finland by the Soviet Union in the Winter War (1939-40), the outcome of which was largely confirmed by the post-1945 Paris Peace Treaties.

A key strength of Paasi's book is its multi-scalar approach. This is combined with an institution- and social practice-based analysis which dramatically illuminates the mutually constitutive role of the international, national, regional, and local level in processes of boundary- and place-making. At a micro level, the book examines the role of the border in the everyday lives and modes of thought of the residents of Värtsilä, a factory commune located in the Eastern province of Karelia. This border region had long played a prominent role in Finnish cultural nationalism. From the nineteenth century, it served as the point of origin for the 'Kalevala', an epic poem rooted in Finnish folklore and mythology. Large swathes of this region were among the territories ceded to the Soviet Union. The Cold War border ran directly through Värtsilä, severing its infrastructure and deeply affecting its inhabitants' local, regional and national identities. Even in the closing years of the Cold War, the 'spatial identities' of the region's inhabitants continued to be influenced by memories of the old commune and utopian images of lost places beyond the closed border. For the younger population of local Finns, meanwhile, the 'here' and 'there' distinction of the boundary came to acquire less emotionally-charged connotations. It increasingly assumed the quality of an unquestioned reality.

Paasi uses an exceptionally broad range of source material to support his argument. The material encompasses school textbooks and academic geography journals as tools of 'spatial socialization'. It also includes newspapers, diaries, travelogues, poems and novels, as well as visual sources such as maps, paintings, advertising posters and photographs (both historical and taken by the author, often set in juxtaposition). These provide the basis for an elucidation of processes of 'socio-spatial integration and distinction'.[62] Finally, the book comprises survey data collected by geographers, anthropologists, and political scientists, as well as material gathered in fieldwork and interviews conducted by the author himself. This innovative combination of various source materials, modes of interpretation, and geographical scales has helped to make Paasi's book a key reference point in scholarly discussions on territoriality, borders and spatial identities.

---

[62] Paasi, *Territories, Boundaries and Consciousness*, pp. 7-15.

# 2 Nature, Environment, and Landscape

William Cronon is responsible for some of the most remarkable 'boundary spanning', spatially engaged scholarship. Today, Cronon holds a professorship in history, geography, and environmental studies – a most telling combination of disciplines. Cronon's 1983 book *Changes in the Land* became one of the early classics of environmental history. This field emerged as a self-conscious field during the 1970s in North America, where it remains particularly strong.[63] The book explores the ecological impact of Native Americans and colonists on New England. At an early stage in the evolution of his research programme, Cronon warned against a common depiction of the relationship between humanity and nature. As he put it: 'The choice is not between two landscapes, one with and one without a human influence; it is between two human ways of living, two ways of belonging to an ecosystem.'[64]

This quotation hints at the three conceptual directions which guide Cronon's book. First, he critiques depictions of a formerly primeval natural landscape in New England, blissfully separate from human influence. Such depictions can be found in the work of early colonists, through to Henry David Thoreau, and even today, they continue to be drawn. Second, Cronon demonstrates how certain *conceptualisations of the land* were fundamental to understanding change – both in the land itself, and in the communities that interacted with it. These conceptualisations included, for example, ideas about bounded property, or differing systems of usage rights. Finally, Cronon's book reveals how these changes about their mutually inhabited spaces both conditioned and were themselves produced by the evolving relationship between Native Americans and colonists.

---

[63] William Cronon, *Changes in the Land: Indians, Colonists, and the Ecology of New England*, New York: Hill and Wang, 2003, first published 1983; for alternative perspectives on the origins of the field beyond North America, see Richard H. Grove, 'Environmental History', in Peter Burke (ed.), *New Perspectives in Historical Writing*, 2nd ed., Cambridge: Polity, 2001, first published 1991, pp. 261-82; J.R. McNeill, 'Observations on the Nature and Culture of Environmental History', *History and Theory* 42 (Theme Issue), 2003, 5-43; for an overview of the field, see Andrew C. Isenberg (ed.), *The Oxford Handbook of Environmental History*, Oxford: Oxford University Press, 2017; and J. Donald Hughes, *What is Environmental History?*, 2nd ed., Cambridge: Polity, 2016; for a concise introduction see John Morgan, 'Environmental History', in Sasha Handley, Rohan McWilliam and Lucy Noakes (eds.), *New Directions in Social and Cultural History*, London: Bloomsbury, 2018, pp. 213-31.

[64] Cronon, *Changes in the Land*, p. 12.

Cronon's 1983 classic highlights two key ingredients for the practice of spatial history. First, it is marked by an understanding of space which does not permit a clear segregation of its material and conceptual aspects. Second, we see an exploration of cultural practices as both constrained by, and productive sources of change in, the land due to the interaction of human and non-human actors. Cronon would go on to refine and sharpen his arguments in a famous 1995 article on 'the trouble with wilderness' – namely, the 'dualistic vision' which presented the wilderness of pristine nature as distinct from human intervention. This concept suggests a divide between humanity and nature which, Cronon argued, is misleading. This 'landscape of authenticity', he clarified, constitutes an attempt to 'escape' from history, a history that includes the development of cultures of the sublime and romantic primitivism.[65]

The way in which we perceive nature and the wilderness is loaded with consequences. Not the least of these consequences is the impact on Indigenous communities which are displaced in the name of conservation.[66] It also, however, lays a foundation for our broader relationship with the world around us. In *The Death of Nature* (1980), Carolyn Merchant, another key early figure in the field of environmental history, explored the impact of changing gendered perceptions of nature: from the image of a nurturing mother earth that represents an organic order towards one of a mechanistic order with nature depicted as a woman who is disorderly, insolent, and corrupting.[67] Building on this work in her *Reinventing Eden* (2003), Merchant offered a history of 'recovery

---

[65] William Cronon, 'The Trouble with Wilderness; or, Getting Back to the Wrong Nature', in id. (ed.), *Uncommon Ground: Rethinking the Human Place in Nature*, New York: W.W. Norton, 1995, 69-90, here p. 80. For an overview of some of the debates around this see J. Baird Callicott and Michael P. Nelson (eds.), *The Great New Wilderness Debate*, Athens: University of Georgia Press, 1998; id. (eds.), *The Wilderness Debate Rages On: Continuing the Great New Wilderness Debate*, Athens: University of Georgia Press, 2008; Donald Worster, 'Seeing Beyond Culture', *The Journal of American History* 76, 1990, 1142-7; as well as the responses to Cronon in the very first issue of *Environmental History* 1/1, 1996.

[66] For examples see Mark David Spence, *Dispossessing the Wilderness: Indian Removal and the Making of the National Parks*, Oxford: Oxford University Press, 2000; Jane Carruthers, *The Kruger National Park: A Social and Political History*, Pietermaritzburg: University of Natal Press, 1995; Roderick P. Neumann, *Imposing Wilderness: Struggles Over Livelihood and Nature Preservation in Africa*, Berkeley: University of California Press, 1998; François G. Richard, *Reluctant Landscapes: Historical Anthropologies of Political Experience in Siin, Senegal*, Chicago and London: University of Chicago Press, 2019; and Jan Bender Shetler, *Imagining Serengeti: A History of Landscape Memory in Tanzania from Earliest Times to the Present*, Athens: Ohio University Press, 2007.

[67] Carolyn Merchant, *The Death of Nature: Women, Ecology, and the Scientific Revolution*, New York: Harper & Row, 1980, p. 133.

narratives' that have attempted to recreate the lost garden of paradise by locating this utopian space in the here and now.[68]

The contradictions between imperatives of conservation and restoration, as well as critiques of the language of conquest and domination over nature, are a central recurring theme in the literature of environmental history. In fact, these tendencies parallel the process by which spaces acquire or lose their status as 'natural'. In *Conquest of Nature* (2006), for example, David Blackbourn focuses on modern German history to trace recurring attempts at 'internal conquest'. These have comprised the draining of 'disorderly' marshlands, the 'taming' of rivers, and the construction of dams. Blackbourn's book lays bare the tragic, often unintended consequences of engineers trying to 'fix' nature or impose 'order' on it.[69] Nancy Langston has pointed in a similar direction in her history of the riparian realm – spaces where land and water combine – of the Malheur Lake Basin in Oregon. As she argues in *Where Land and Water Meet* (2003), wilderness restoration efforts in this region gave rise to an 'empire of ducks'. This was the consequence of favouring one species within a complex ecosystem, as drained wetlands were reflooded to restore ducks' breeding areas.[70] Clearly, conflicts *between* visions for the protection of natural or 'wild' spaces, and not

---

[68] id., *Reinventing Eden: The Fate of Nature in Western Culture*, New York: Routledge, 2003; for examples of exploring close relationship between conceptions of nature and material consequences in a non-Western context, see Julia Adeney Thomas, *Reconfiguring Modernity: Concepts of Nature in Japanese Political Ideology*, Berkeley: University of California Press, 2001; Judith Shapiro, *Mao's War against Nature: Politics and the Environment in Revolutionary China*, Cambridge: Cambridge University Press, 2001; and Jonathan Schlesinger, *A World Trimmed with Fur: Wild Things, Pristine Places, and the Natural Fringes of Qing Rule*, Stanford: Stanford University Press, 2017.

[69] David Blackbourn, *The Conquest of Nature: Water, Landscape and the Making of Modern Germany*, London: Jonathan Cape, 2006, p. 13. Sticking with work on engineering water, see also Richard White, *The Organic Machine: The Remaking of the Columbia River*, New York: Hill and Wang, 1995; Chris Courtney, *The Nature of Disaster in China: The 1931 Yangzi River Flood*, Cambridge: Cambridge University Press, 2018; Maya K. Peterson, *Pipe Dreams: Water and Empire in Central Asia's Aral Sea Basin*, Cambridge: Cambridge University Press, 2020; Alan Mikhail, *Nature and Empire in Ottoman Egypt: An Environmental History*, Cambridge: Cambridge University Press, 2011; Dilip da Cunha, *The Invention of Rivers: Alexander's Eye and Ganga's Descent*, Philadelphia: University of Pennsylvania Press, 2019; Julia Obertreis, *Imperial Desert Dreams: Cotton Growing and Irrigation in Central Asia, 1860–1991*, Göttingen: V&R Unipress, 2017; Nicholas B. Breyfogle (ed.), *Eurasian Environments: Nature and Ecology in Imperial Russian and Soviet History*, Pittsburgh, PA: University of Pittsburgh Press, 2018; see also the chapter by Mark Harris in Bavaj, Lawson and Struck (eds.), *Doing Spatial History*.

[70] Nancy Langston, *Where Land and Water Meet: A Western Landscape Transformed*, Seattle and London: University of Washington Press, 2003; see also Fredrik Albritton Jonsson, *Enlightenment's Frontier: The Scottish Highlands and the Origins of Environmentalism*, New Haven: Yale University Press, 2013.

merely between conservation and other human uses of the land, play out in many changing landscapes.

This concept of a 'landscape' is employed in all the works of environmental history mentioned above and is a key term for spatial history.[71] It is one of the most elusive but also 'boundary spanning' of concepts. It has deep roots in the disciplines of geography and art history, and it is widely embraced in anthropology, architecture, urban studies, history, and literary studies. That said, and as Tim Cresswell has pointed out, it is also a concept heavily 'burdened with its own history – too fixed on origins'.[72] To ask what the term 'landscape' means, one must usually contend with the multiple accounts of its lineage. The long view can lead back through the history of landscape art to Renaissance culture and the aesthetics of linear perspective. Alternatively, as Kenneth Olwig has argued, it could proceed via German and Danish conceptions of territory and community.[73] A shorter history of its embrace by geographers might focus on a number of key figures who cast long shadows over the literature, each with very distinct perspectives: Paul Vidal de la Blache (1845-1918), Friedrich Ratzel (1844-1904), Carl Ortwin Sauer (1889-1975), W. G. Hoskins (1908-1992), and J. B. Jackson (1909-1996).[74]

Since the 1970s, historians who have embraced *landscape* as their primary spatial concept have tended to borrow from three approaches developed by geographers. The first of these approaches draws on an argument famously articulated by Denis Cosgrove in his book *Social Formation and Symbolic Landscape* (1984). Cosgrove conceptualises landscapes as a *way of seeing* one's surroundings. This perceptual pattern is in fact the product of a particular historical moment – Renaissance Europe – and a set of changing economic and social relations.[75]

---

[71] See also the chapter by Sherry Olson and Peter Holland in Bavaj, Lawson and Struck (eds.), *Doing Spatial History*.

[72] Tim Cresswell, 'Landscape and the Obliteration of Practice', in Kay Anderson et al. (eds.), *Handbook of Cultural Geography*, London: Sage, 2003, p. 269.

[73] See Denis E. Cosgrove, *Social Formation and Symbolic Landscape*, with a new introduction, Madison: University of Wisconsin Press, 1998, first published 1984, for the former; see Kenneth R. Olwig, 'Recovering the Substantive Nature of Landscape', *Annals of the Association of American Geographers* 86, 1996, 630–53, for a short account of the latter.

[74] For a survey, see John Wylie, *Landscape*, London and New York: Routledge, 2007; Matthew Johnson, *Ideas of Landscape*, Malden, Mass.: Blackwell, 2007; and the shorter overview by Veronica della Dora, 'Landscape and History', in Mona Domosh, Michael Heffernan and Charles W.J. Withers (eds.), *The SAGE Handbook of Historical Geography*, vol. 1, London: Sage, 2020, pp. 121-42.

[75] Cosgrove, *Social Formation and Symbolic Landscape*, p. 1; see also id., *The Palladian Landscape: Geographical Change and Its Cultural Representations in Sixteenth-Century Italy*, Leicester: Leicester

In publications spanning most of his career, Cosgrove used vision as the means to explore historical terrain. He often did this through close analysis of visual sources, from art to architectural drawings and cartography.[76]

A second approach holds that a landscape, in the form of rural and urban environments, constitutes a 'signifying system' that may be *read like a text*. This is most clearly articulated in the article '(Re)Reading the Landscape' by James and Nancy Duncan, and in *The City as Text* (1990) by James Duncan.[77] These contributions draw on a range of tools from literary analysis. They show that a discourse about a landscape may be 'denaturalised' through an analysis of its rhetorical features. These include tropes such as allegory, synecdoche and metonymy, and the 'intertextuality' represented by the relationship between a landscape discourse and both other texts and social practices.[78] For the historian, the overriding goal of such an analysis is to better understand the dominant ideologies and the cultural relationships of power within a given society. In *The Reformation of the Landscape* (2012), moreover, Alexandra Walsham has shown how writers in sixteenth- and seventeenth-century Britain and Ireland themselves thought of the landscape as a text, and as a system of symbols, which might be decoded.[79]

A third conceptual tool comprises a phenomenological approach which emphasises the embedded nature of humanity in a landscape that is produced by experience and practice. This tendency has come in two separate waves. The first of these waves came during the 1970s in the work of 'humanistic' geographers. Edward Relph, for example, framed landscape as 'the visual contexts of daily existence'.[80] Similarly, Yi-Fu Tuan saw landscape as an

University Press, 1993. Compare with the introduction by Cosgrove and Daniels in Denis Cosgrove and Stephen Daniels (eds.), *The Iconography of Landscape: Essays on the Symbolic Representation, Design and Use of Past Environments*, Cambridge: Cambridge University Press, 1988, pp. 1-10; for an important feminist critique of the visual gaze in the study of landscapes see Gillian Rose, *Feminism and Geography: The Limits of Geographical Knowledge*, Cambridge: Polity, 1993, pp. 86-112.

[76] See, for example, the essay collection by Denis Cosgrove, *Geography and Vision: Seeing, Imagining and Representing the World*, London and New York: I.B. Tauris, 2008. This approach continues to inspire innovative work, including Nobuko Toyosawa, *Imaginative Mapping: Landscape and Japanese Identity in the Tokugawa and Meiji Eras*, Cambridge, Mass.: Harvard University Asia Center, 2019.

[77] Nancy Duncan and James Duncan, '(Re)Reading the Landscape', *Environment and Planning D: Society and Space* 6/2, 1988, 117–26.

[78] James S. Duncan, *The City as Text: The Politics of Landscape Interpretation in the Kandyan Kingdom*, Cambridge: Cambridge University Press, 1990, pp. 15-24.

[79] Alexandra Walsham *The Reformation of the Landscape: Religion, Identity, and Memory in Early Modern Britain and Ireland*, Oxford: Oxford University Press, 2012, pp. 5-6.

[80] Edward Relph, *The Modern Urban Landscape*, London: Croom Helm, 1987, p. 3; see also his

'ordering of reality' undertaken by a subject located within that very landscape – to inevitably combine the objective and subjective 'through an effort of the imagination exercised over a highly selected array of sense data'.[81]

A further wave of phenomenological approaches to landscapes was evident in the work of social anthropologist Tim Ingold, and in the work of archaeologist Christopher Tilley, who built on Ingold's contributions.[82] Ingold critiqued the 'insistent dualism' of object and subject. This was, he argued, implicit in Cosgrove's visual metaphor, and even in Tuan's depiction of the landscape as something found within the mind.[83] Instead, Ingold draws on the metaphor of 'weaving', or a 'movement of incorporation' of our practices and our environment. Against this background, the landscape is seen as 'a pattern of activities "collapsed" into an array of features'.[84] These collapsed 'features' are not merely physical objects we might point to, nor are they a network of distinct places linked together in a path of cumulative experiences. After all, we may see the landscape as a whole in any given place. This is because landscape's describable features are 'woven' into the product of cumulative human activity, which Ingold refers to as the 'taskscape'. Landscape is thus an aggregation neither of elements 'out there', nor of the floating strands of memory and imagined space assembled in the mind.

The art historian W. J. T. Mitchell has shown himself to be similarly concerned with cultural practice. In his introduction to *Landscape and Power* (1994), Mitchell proposed that the word 'landscape' could meaningfully be changed 'from a noun to a verb'. He asked 'that we think of landscape, not as an object to be seen or a text to be read, but as a process by which social and subjective identities are formed'.[85]

---

earlier id., *Place and Placelessness*, London: Pion, 1976; and id., *Rational Landscapes and Humanistic Geography*, London: Croom Helm, 1981.

[81] Yi-Fu Tuan, 'Thought and Landscape: The Eye and the Mind's Eye', in D.W. Meinig (ed.), *The Interpretation of Ordinary Landscapes: Geographical Essays*, Oxford: Oxford University Press, 1979, pp. 89-102, here p. 90; see also id., *Landscapes of Fear*, New York: Pantheon Books, 1979.

[82] See Tim Ingold, *The Perception of the Environment: Essays on Livelihood, Dwelling and Skill*, London: Routledge, 2000, esp. ch. 3: 'Hunting and gathering as ways of perceiving the environment', and chapter 11: 'The temporality of the landscape'; see also Christopher Tilley, *A Phenomenology of Landscape: Places, Paths and Monuments*, Oxford: Berg, 1994; Wylie, *Landscape*, pp. 139-86; for an example of work inspired by Ingold's approach, see Fei Huang, *Reshaping the Frontier Landscape: Dongchuan in Eighteenth-Century Southwest China*, Leiden: Brill, 2018.

[83] Ingold, *Perception of the Environment*, pp. 190-3.

[84] Ibid., p. 198.

[85] W. J. T. Mitchell (ed.), *Landscape and Power*, 2nd ed., Chicago and London: University of Chicago Press, 2002, first published 1994, p. 1; see also the chapter by Dawn Hollis in Bavaj,

30

David Matless is one of many geographers to have taken their cue from Mitchell. In his book *Landscape and Englishness* (1998), Matless draws on an evolving senses of Englishness between 1918 to the 1950s to show how landscape 'shuttles through temporal processes of history and memory'.[86] He analyses the history of two contrasting visions of the relationship between landscape and English identity: an emerging doctrine of preservation allied with modernism, and a separate counter-current of an organic England focused on soil and authority. However, Matless' approach is most distinguished by its combination of two separate intellectual moves. First, his book offers an analysis of discourses around the landscape in images and text. At the same time, it provides a history of the practices that formed these landscapes through lived experience. And so we encounter rural ramblers, conservative Scouts, and socialist Woodcraft Folk in motion across the moorland, or an organicist expanding humus production in the countryside.[87] These are all important components of the formation of 'cultures of landscape' – and certainly as important as any laudatory account of these practices from a distance at some fixed moment in time.

Elsewhere in historical writing, landscapes are often closely associated with a more or less clearly articulated spatial imaginary. One example is the hugely capacious German concept of *Heimat*, or homeland. Tracing this idea across time reveals it as the product of contestation among individuals and institutions, or in everyday practice. This is certainly not conducive to a static view, and it necessitates a focus on what these landscapes are 'doing'. Celia Applegate argues that the utility of *Heimat* has been 'its capacity to obscure any chasms between small local worlds and the larger ones to which the locality belonged'.[88] That said, the concept has not proven infinitely flexible. Frank Uekötter has examined the history of *Heimat* and its place in landscape protection campaigns during the Nazi period and argues that the concept's deployment by the Nazi

---

Lawson and Struck (eds.), *Doing Spatial History*.

[86] David Matless, *Landscape and Englishness*, London: Reaktion, 1998, pp. 13-14; for the 'long nineteenth century', see Paul Readman, *Storied Ground: Landscape and the Shaping of English National Identity*, Cambridge: Cambridge University Press, 2018; the 'multi-vocality of landscape' is teased out in a more recent book by David Matless, *In the Nature of Landscape: Cultural Geography on the Norfolk Broads*, Malden, Mass.: Blackwell, 2014.

[87] Matless, *Landscape and Englishness*, pp. 70-9, 106-7.

[88] Celia Applegate, *A Nation of Provincials: The German Idea of Heimat*, Berkeley: University of California Press, 1990, p. 10.

state was severely limited by its diffuse and persistently regional, as opposed to merely national, resonances.[89]

Landscapes feature prominently in the history of colonial spaces. This is not only because of what can be found in such spaces, but also what is missing from them. In Mary Louise Pratt's *Imperial Eyes* (1992), we see how travellers 'naturalized' the African landscape in their accounts: 'Where, one asks, is everybody?'[90] Similarly, David Hughes shows how white settlers in Zimbabwe 'imagine[d] the natives away' in their early attempts to negotiate an identity with the land.[91] David Arnold's *Tropics and the Traveling Gaze* (2006) drew explicitly on Carter's *Road to Botany Bay* (1987) in describing itself as a work of spatial history. This book embraces Pratt's focus on the 'ocular authority of the traveller' and identifies two evolving European ways of seeing the Indian landscape – one romantic and one scientific – which together constituted expressions of 'tropicality'.[92] The geographical imaginary described by Said's

[89] Frank Uekötter, *The Green and the Brown: A History of Conservation in Nazi Germany*, Cambridge: Cambridge University Press, 2006, p. 20; see also Alon Confino, *The Nation as a Local Metaphor: Württemberg, Imperial Germany, and National Memory, 1871-1918*, Chapel Hill and London: University of North Carolina Press, 1997; Elizabeth Boa and Rachel Palfreyman, *Heimat – A German Dream: Regional Loyalties and National Identity in German Culture, 1890-1990*, Oxford: Oxford University Press, 2000; Thomas M. Lekan, *Imagining the Nation in Nature: Landscape Preservation and German Identity 1885-1945*, Cambridge, Mass.: Harvard University Press, 2004; Thomas Zeller, *Driving Germany: The Landscape of the German Autobahn, 1930-1970*, Oxford: Berghahn, 2007; and Friederike Eigler, 'Critical Approaches to "Heimat" and the "Spatial Turn"', *New German Critique* 115, 2012, 27–48.

[90] Mary Louise Pratt, *Imperial Eyes: Travel Writing and Transculturation*, London and New York: Routledge, 1992; for the way colonial landscapes are gendered, see also Sara Mills, *Gender and Colonial Space*, Manchester: Manchester University Press, 2005.

[91] David McDermott Hughes, *Whiteness in Zimbabwe: Race, Landscape, and the Problem of Belonging*, New York: Palgrave Macmillan, 2010, p. xii; see also William M. Adams and Martin Mulligan (eds.), *Decolonizing Nature: Strategies for Conservation in a Post-Colonial Era*, London: Earthscan Publications, 2003.

[92] David Arnold, *The Tropics and the Traveling Gaze: India, Landscape, and Science, 1800-1856*, Seattle and London: University of Washington Press, 2006, pp. 3, 24; on tropicality see also Gavin Bowd and Daniel Clayton, *Impure and Worldly Geography: Pierre Gourou and Tropicality*, London and New York: Routledge, 2019; Alan Bewell, *Romanticism and Colonial Disease*, Baltimore: Johns Hopkins University Press, 1999; Jiat-Hwee Chang, *A Genealogy of Tropical Architecture: Colonial Networks, Nature and Technoscience*, London and New York: Routledge, 2016; Felix Driver and Luciana Martins, *Tropical Visions in an Age of Empire*, Chicago and London: University of Chicago Press, 2005; Nancy Leys Stepan, *Picturing Tropical Nature*, London: Reaktion, 2001. Tropicality is also tied closely to the environmental politics of empire. See Corey Ross, *Ecology and Power in the Age of Empire: Europe and the Transformation of the Tropical World*, Oxford: Oxford University Press, 2017; Richard H. Grove, *Green Imperialism: Colonial Expansion, Tropical Island Edens, and the Origins of Environmentalism, 1600-1860*, Cambridge: Cambridge University Press, 1995; Peder Anker, *Imperial Ecology: Environmental Order in the British Empire, 1895-1945*, Cambridge, Mass.: Harvard

'Orientalism' situates a particular space – the 'Orient' – within a stagnant temporal frame by means of its views on culture. Conversely, Arnold suggests that 'tropicality' is a better way to capture the equally essentialized approach to the diverse Indian landscape as 'warm, fecund, luxuriant, paradisiacal and pestilential.'[93]

In contrast to the landscapes described in European travel literature or in paintings, other historians have adapted the concept to capture Indigenous perspectives. Notable here is Jan Bender Shetler's *Imagining Serengeti* (2007), a history of the 'memory landscape' of the western Serengeti in Tanzania. Shetler develops a unique methodology for the 'spatial analysis of oral tradition'. This aims to reconnect 'core images' in the memories of the region's peoples to the places and spatial practices in and around today's Serengeti National Park.[94] The approach goes well beyond transcription and analysis of an oral record, as Shetler follows the Serengeti peoples to the places featured in their images of the past. The result is a powerful account which traces the creation of the famous nature park. This is often depicted as one of the world's wildest spaces. In fact, it has merely erased the human from its history.

## Nature's Metropolis

Let us take a closer look at one of the key works which aptly exemplifies many of these theoretical reflections. Between the publication of *Changes in the Land* in 1983 and 'The Trouble with Wilderness' in 1995, William Cronon wrote the award-winning work *Nature's Metropolis: Chicago and the Great West* (1991). It exhibits a deep and explicit engagement with space. Cronon describes his book as a 'series of stories, each tracing the path between an urban market and natural systems that supply it'. But this does not do justice to the ambition of the work.[95] Cronon explores the writings of 'boosters', authors of promotional

---

University Press, 2001; David Arnold and Ramachandra Guha (eds.), *Nature, Culture, Imperialism: Essays on the Environmental History of South Asia*, Oxford: Oxford University Press, 1995.

[93] Arnold, *Tropics and the Traveling Gaze*, p. 7.

[94] Shetler, *Imagining Serengeti*, pp. 18-25; on African landscapes see also David William Cohen and E. S. Atieno Odhiambo, *Siaya: The Historical Anthropology of an African Landscape*, London: Currey, 1989; Ute Luig and Achim von Oppen, 'Landscape in Africa: Process and Vision', *Paideuma* 43, 1997, 7–45; Alison Blunt, *Travel, Gender, and Imperialism: Mary Kingsley and West Africa*, New York: Guilford Press, 1994; Melissa Leach and Robin Mearns, *The Lie of the Land: Challenging Received Wisdom on the African Environment*, Oxford: International African Institute, 1996; Howard and Shain (eds.), *The Spatial Factor in African History*.

[95] William Cronon, *Nature's Metropolis: Chicago and the Great West*, New York: W.W. Norton, 1991, p. xv.

literature who sought to establish Chicago's position as a great 'Central City' at the heart of America. He goes on to recount the development of canal and rail networks that tied the city to its hinterland and Eastern markets. He also includes chapters on grain, lumber, and meat markets, debt networks, supplying retail merchants, as well as the 1893 Columbian Exposition. The chapters abound with microhistories. We learn of the rise of grain elevators, meat disassembly lines, and mail order catalogues, among other things. But the chapters serve a broader purpose of capturing an interconnected series of relationships, all of which are tied to questions of spatial import.

The spatial aspects of Cronon's book can be seen most clearly in three areas. First, the book repeatedly engages with perceptions of Chicago that alternatively see it as part of, or separate from, its surrounding environment. Throughout the book, 'nature' is a flexible metaphor deployed in multiple ways by a range of figures. For example, farmers or other visitors to the city – including Cronon when he was a child – depict nature as 'a nonhuman creation damaged and endangered' by the city. Others, however, invoke nature as a 'nonhuman power which called this place into being and enabled its heroic inhabitants to perform their extraordinary feats'.[96] This is what Cronon would later refer to as 'nature as moral imperative', an inexorable hand of fate leaving no room for alternative outcomes.[97]

Secondly, the book's various case studies expose the wholly illusory nature of a division between rural and urban landscapes. Instead, these become single, completely interdependent systems. They are 'not two places but one. They created each other, they transformed each other's environments and economies, and they now depend on each other for their very survival.'[98] We are presented with a process of abstraction. This emerges through the transformation of grain into *liquid* gold, detached from any connection to a specific farmer and their field, or refrigerated beef detached in time and space from its traditional seasonal availability and point of origin. This is redolent of what Marx called an 'annihilation of space', but also of nature: 'Meat was a neatly wrapped package one bought at the market. Nature did not have much to do with it.'[99]

Finally, *Nature's Metropolis* plays with the ironic contradictions which inevitably arise when we are confronted by the striking centrality of the

---

[96] Ibid., p. 14.

[97] William Cronon, 'Introduction', in id. (ed.), *Uncommon Ground*, p. 36.

[98] Cronon, *Nature's Metropolis*, p. 384.

[99] Ibid., p. 257.

assumedly peripheral. Chicago, for example, was both at the centre and on the edge. Cronon shows how Chicago necessitates an inverse reading of Frederick Jackson Turner famous frontier thesis. Turner envisioned a gradual 'disintegration of savagery' on the margins of pioneer conquest. Instead, we find that the explosive growth of a new 'central' metropolis provides the opening chapter of a developmental story, rather than its triumphal conclusion.[100]

Overall, the concept of space draws together the component elements of *Nature's Metropolis* – not unlike the tangle of railways flowing into the 'central' city of Chicago. The economic, environmental, and intellectual history facets of the work each contribute to a holistic understanding of the contradictory and evolving conceptions of nature and frontier that it so illuminatingly explores.

---

[100] Ibid., p. 32.

# 3 City and Home

It may seem arbitrary to single out the city and home as locales for spatial history. There is, after all, no shortage of alternatives, such as oceans, bridges, and teahouses.[101] The special consideration of city and home is merited, however, by their considerable prominence in scholarship that foregrounds space and place.

Many key theoretical engagements with space have drawn chiefly on the examples of city or home. The city is usually the assumed scale of analysis in Lefebvre's *Production of Space* (1974), with Venice offering the most concrete case explored in the book.[102] Walter Benjamin's studies are notable for their exploration of the urban fabric of Paris and the street wandering *flâneur* in his Arcades project. This was only the best known of his many philosophically rich works which centre on the city as a space.[103] Edward Soja often turns to Los Angeles to explore the spaces of postmodernity, while Michel de Certeau's most frequently cited passage is taken from his chapter on 'Walking in the City'.[104]

The city also serves as a key site for many other spatial theorists. These include Saskia Sassen, Janet Abu-Lughod, Ash Amin, Nigel Thrift, and Linda McDowell.[105] David Harvey's work in urban geography played an important

---

[101] See, for example, Philip E. Steinberg, *The Social Construction of the Ocean*, Cambridge: Cambridge University Press, 2001; Thomas Harrison, *Of Bridges: A Poetic and Philosophical Account*, Chicago and London: University of Chicago Press, 2021; Di Wang, *The Teahouse: Small Business, Everyday Culture, and Public Politics in Chengdu, 1900-1950*, Stanford: Stanford University Press, 2008.

[102] Henri Lefebvre, *The Production of Space*, trans. Donald Nicholson-Smith, Oxford: Blackwell, 1991, French 1974.

[103] Walter Benjamin worked on this from 1927 until his death in 1940, and it was first published in German in 1982. For an English translation see Walter Benjamin, *The Arcades Project*, trans. Howard Eiland and Kevin McLaughlin, Cambridge, Mass.: Harvard University Press, 1999; for a helpful commentary, see Mike Savage, 'Walter Benjamin's Urban Thought: A Critical Analysis', in Mike Crang and Nigel Thrift (eds.), *Thinking Space*, London and New York: Routledge, 2000, pp. 33–53; as well as Susan Buck-Morss, *The Dialectics of Seeing: Walter Benjamin and the Arcades Project*, Cambridge, Mass. and London: MIT Press, 1989, pp. 25-43. For an important critique of the figure of the flâneur from a gender studies perspective see Aruna D'Souza and Tom McDonough (eds.), *The Invisible Flâneuse? Gender, Public Space, and Visual Culture in Nineteenth-Century Paris*, Manchester: Manchester University Press, 2006.

[104] Edward W. Soja, *Postmodern Geographies: The Reassertion of Space in Critical Social Theory*, 8th ed., London and New York: Verso, 2003, first published 1989; id., *Thirdspace: Journeys to Los Angeles and Other Real-and-Imagined Places*, Malden, Mass.: Blackwell, 1996; Michel de Certeau, *The Practice of Everyday Life*, Berkeley: University of California Press, 1984, French 1980, pp. 91-102.

[105] See Saskia Sassen, *The Global City: New York, London, Tokyo*, Princeton: Princeton University Press, 1991; Ash Amin and Nigel Thrift, *Cities: Reimagining the Urban*, Cambridge: Polity, 2002;

role in introducing Lefebvre to English language readers. He places the 'spatial forms' of the city and the economic workings of 'relational space' in urban life at the centre of his book *Social Justice and the City* (1973).[106] As these examples suggest, many of the best spatial analyses of cities come from well-established sub-disciplines such as urban geography, urban history, architectural history, and urban sociology, or the innately interdisciplinary field of urban studies.[107] The structure of cities, as well as the larger economic regions they form a part of, has also been important to scholarship that adopts more formal methodologies for studying space and social patterns. Some of this work draws inspiration from a long tradition of 'central place theory' and related approaches. This includes the work of the anthropologist and East Asia scholar G. William Skinner, or scholars employing 'space syntax' approaches developed by Bill Hillier, a strong proponent of architectural and urban morphology studies.[108]

What of the home as a unit of analysis? Again, there is no shortage of examples here. We might think of Pierre Bourdieu's analysis of the Berber house as a microcosm of the universe, Gaston Bachelard's 'oneiric' or dreamlike house in *Poetics of Space* (1957), or Martin Heidegger's use of the house as the only manifestation of anything concrete in his famous essay 'Building

---

id., *Seeing Like a City*, Cambridge: Polity, 2017; Janet L. Abu-Lughod, *Cairo: 1001 Years of the City Victorious*, Princeton: Princeton University Press, 1971; Linda McDowell, *Capital Culture: Gender at Work in the City*, Oxford: Blackwell, 1997.

[106] David Harvey, *Social Justice and the City*, London: Edward Arnold, 1973; see also id., *Spaces of Hope*, Edinburgh: Edinburgh University Press, 2000; on Harvey and Lefebvre, see Andy Merrifield, *Henri Lefebvre: A Critical Introduction*, New York and London: Routledge, 2006, p. 102.

[107] To urban studies, the related fields of urban design and urban planning could be added, all of which regularly engage with the other fields mentioned. For how these many urban focused disciplines interact, see the excellent essay by Richard T. LeGates, 'Prologue: How to Study Cities', in id. and Frederic Stout (eds.), *The City Reader*, 7th ed., London: Routledge, 2020, pp. 3-8; for an introduction to urban geography, see Phil Hubbard, *City*, 2nd ed., London: Routledge, 2018. Key figures and texts are surveyed in Regan Koch and Alan Latham (eds.), *Key Thinkers on Cities*, London: Sage, 2017; for urban history, see Shane Ewen, *What is Urban History?*, Cambridge: Polity, 2016; and the growing number of volumes in the *Routledge Advances in Urban History* series (2017-).

[108] See several of Skinner's essays in G. William Skinner, *The City in Late Imperial China*, Stanford: Stanford University Press, 1977; for space syntax, see Bill Hillier and Julienne Hanson, *The Social Logic of Space*, Cambridge: Cambridge University Press, 1984. Examples of this scholarship can be seen in Laura Vaughan, *Mapping Society: The Spatial Dimensions of Social Cartography*, London: UCL Press, 2018; Sam Griffiths and Alexander von Lünen (eds.), *Spatial Cultures: Towards a New Social Morphology of Cities Past and Present*, London: Routledge, 2016. For approaches to social space from the air, see Jeanne Haffner, *The View from Above: The Science of Social Space*, Cambridge, Mass.: MIT Press, 2013.

Dwelling Thinking' (1951). These examples show how the home, like the city, has been important in anthropological and philosophical works that have heavily influenced the study of space and place among historians.[109]

Scholarship on the home as a space has received the widest engagement within at least four overlapping conceptual approaches. First, the home has long been key to an anthropological analysis of culture.[110] Second, architectural historians have frequently explored the structure, form, interiors, and architectural discourses around social practice.[111] Third, historians of everyday life, of emotions and the senses, as well as scholars who explore interior spaces as they appear in literature, have contributed immensely to the study of the home.[112] Fourth – and perhaps most significantly – histories of the home and domestic space have been at the core of interdisciplinary debates around gender.[113] There has been a marked departure from simplistic and often highly

---

[109] Pierre Bourdieu, 'The Berber House or the World Reversed', *Social Science Information* 9/2, 1970, 151–70; Gaston Bachelard, *The Poetics of Space*, Boston: Beacon Press, 1994, French 1957; Martin Heidegger, 'Building Dwelling Thinking' (1951), in Sharon M. Meagher (ed.), *Philosophy and the City: Classic to Contemporary Writings*, New York: SUNY Press, 2008, pp. 119-25. A broad survey of the literature on the home is provided by Alison Blunt and Robyn Dowling, *Home*, London: Routledge, 2006. Many key writings can be found in Chiara Briganti and Kathy Mezei (eds.), *The Domestic Space Reader*, Toronto: University of Toronto Press, 2012.

[110] A good starting point to this anthropological literature is the essay by Farhan Samanani and Johannes Lenhard, 'House and Home', 2019, in *Cambridge Encyclopedia of Anthropology*. Available HTTP: <https://www.anthroencyclopedia.com/entry/house-and-home> (accessed 19 March 2021). Although not limited to contributions from anthropologists, see also the collection by Irene Cieraad (ed.), *At Home: An Anthropology of Domestic Space*, Syracuse: Syracuse University Press, 1999.

[111] See examples of these approaches in Paul Oliver, *Built to Meet Needs: Cultural Issues in Vernacular Architecture*, Amsterdam: Elsevier, 2006; and works such as Annmarie Adams, *Architecture in the Family Way: Doctors, Houses, and Women, 1870-1900*, Montreal: McGill-Queen's University Press, 1996; Alice T. Friedman, *Women and the Making of the Modern House: A Social and Architectural History*, New York: Harry N. Abrams, 1998; and Carla Yanni, *Living on Campus: An Architectural History of the American Dormitory*, Minneapolis: University of Minnesota Press, 2019. Architectural aspects of the home are often addressed by scholars in neighbouring disciplines, such as in the works by archaeologist Matthew Johnson, *Housing Culture: Traditional Architecture in an English Landscape*, London: UCL Press, 1993; and id., *English Houses 1300-1800: Vernacular Architecture, Social Life*, London and New York: Routledge, 2010; see also the chapter by Despina Stratigakos in Bavaj, Lawson and Struck (eds.), *Doing Spatial History*.

[112] For an extensive survey, especially on Europe and North America, see the six volumes in the series by Amanda Flather (ed.), *A Cultural History of the Home*, London: Bloomsbury, 2021.

[113] Some of the key works in this area include Rose, *Feminism and Geography;* Daphne Spain, *Gendered Spaces*, Chapel Hill: University of North Carolina Press, 1992; Shirley Ardener (ed.), *Women and Space: Ground Rules and Social Maps*, 2nd rev. ed., Oxford: Berg, 1993, first published 1981; Dorothy O. Helly and Susan M. Reverby, *Gendered Domains: Rethinking Public and Private in Women's History*, Ithaca: Cornell University Press, 1992; David Morley, *Home Territories: Media, Mobility and Identity*, London: Routledge, 2000; Sarah Pink, *Home Truths: Gender, Domestic Objects*

critical accounts of the home as a 'private' feminine space. Many of the assumptions and binary oppositions of earlier work have yielded to new perspectives. These have encompassed a more careful and consistent distinction between *house* and *home*; a more sceptical approach towards the home as a *private* space; a more nuanced understanding of *power* and *agency* in the domestic sphere; and a questioning of gendered stereotypes of specific rooms, or of the home as a whole. But this is to cover only some of the ways in which the home has hosted an active and evolving historiography.[114]

Let us now survey some of the main themes in the scholarship on city and home which most firmly foreground space and place. If we begin with perceptions of the city itself, we might start with American urban planner Kevin Lynch's *The Image of the City* (1960).[115] This influential work was based in large part on the analysis of a series of lengthy interviews with residents of Boston, Jersey City, and Los Angeles.[116] Lynch built a collective cognitive map of each city. He used these cognitive maps to embark on a reading of paths, edges (recognisable boundaries), districts (areas of two-dimensional extents), nodes (strategic spots that help orient an observer), and landmarks. Lynch argued that, together, these elements composed an image of a more or less 'imageable' city. They helped to define the city's form as expressed in the degree of its singularity (sharpness of boundaries), simplicity and clarity, perception of continuity, the dominance of particular city components, and so forth. Certainly, Lynch drew on a formalised method. However, his raw material was derived from the memories of individuals who live in and move through the city regularly. Without needing to embrace the same formal typology, a

---

and *Everyday Life*, Oxford: Berg, 2004; K. H. Adler and Carrie Hamilton (eds.), *Homes and Homecomings: Gendered Histories of Domesticity and Return*, Oxford: Wiley-Blackwell, 2010; Joachim Eibach and Margareth Lanzinger (eds.), *The Routledge History of the Domestic Sphere in Europe: 16th to 19th Century*, London and New York: Routledge, 2020; John Tosh, *A Man's Place: Masculinity and the Middle-Class Home in Victorian England*, New Haven: Yale University Press, 1999; and Antoinette Burton, *Dwelling in the Archive: Women Writing House, Home, and History in Late Colonial India*, Oxford: Oxford University Press, 2003.

[114] For a survey of some of these debates, see Shelley Mallett, 'Understanding Home: A Critical Review of the Literature', *The Sociological Review* 52/1, 2004, 62–89.

[115] Kevin Lynch, *The Image of the City*, Cambridge, Mass. and London: MIT Press, 1960. For an example of how historical GIS is employed to understanding spatial relations see Richard Rodger and Susanne Rau, 'Thinking Spatially: New Horizons for Urban History', *Urban History* 47 (2020), 372–83.

[116] For a historical take on the cases of evolving form, see Mona Domosh, *Invented Cities: The Creation of Landscape in Nineteenth-Century New York and Boston*, New Haven: Yale University Press, 1996.

historian may be inspired to analyse these 'tours,' as de Certeau called the narrative 'spatial stories' of our everyday life. They could provide the basis for an exploration of the spatial sensibilities of subjects found in a wide range of sources, from diaries to literary works.[117]

A cognitive map of one's lived experience in the city is only one of many possible approaches to exploring perceptions of urban space. The totality of the city is the object of a broad range of discourses, as can be seen in literary depictions of the city. This dimension was explored in British author and critic Raymond Williams' *The Country and the City* (1973), especially as characters in novels move from the former to the latter, or else compare them.[118] Williams was especially interested in tracing changes in these views over time. For instance, he argued that an earlier 'perceptual confusion and ambivalence' towards the city characterised the poems of, say, William Wordsworth. Over time, however, this ambivalence evolved into the view that cities helped to produce an intense sense of alienation.

Williams argued that there was a perceived human 'dissolution in the very process of aggregation' in the industrialised city. This is evident in the novels of Charles Dickens, or the writings of Friedrich Engels and Karl Marx.[119] Indeed, we may trace these changing views across the work of myriad figures who have studied the city's relationship to humanity. The sociologist Georg Simmel, for example, argued that the city produces a 'metropolitan type' of human endowed with techniques to protect their inner life. Conversely, the writer, philosopher and architectural critic Lewis Mumford suggested that, though the city might lead to 'personal disintegration', it was also to be celebrated as a wondrous 'theatre of social activity'.[120] The city as an array of evolving signifiers is a rich feature in the history of cultural discourses. These range from the socialist Charles Fourier's view of Paris as a 'manufactory of putrefaction' due to its poverty and disease, or Miklós Horthy's depiction of Budapest as the 'sinful city', through to the ethnographic exoticism of Lafcadio Hearn's depictions of late-nineteenth-century New Orleans, or the 'marvellous atmosphere of a great birth' witnessed by journalist Grace Ellison's in 1920s Angora (Ankara).[121] Tracing and comparing these discourses are effective ways

---

[117] De Certeau, *The Practice of Everyday Life*, pp. 118-9.

[118] Raymond Williams, *The Country and the City*, London: Chatto and Windus, 1973.

[119] Ibid., p. 311.

[120] Georg Simmel, 'The Metropolis and Mental Life', in Meagher (ed.), *Philosophy and the City*, pp. 96-101, here p. 97; Lewis Mumford, 'What is a City?', *Architectural Record* 82, 1937, 59-62.

[121] Charles Fourier, quoted in Andrew Lees, *Cities Perceived: Urban Society in European and American*

of understanding our changing spatial relationship with any sizeable human community. They have been prominent features of scholarship in multiple fields.[122]

One of the most enduring concepts linked to the image of the city has been that of 'modernity'. This has frequently been closely associated with the impact of capitalism.[123] Carl Schorske's *Fin-de-Siècle Vienna* (1979) explored an emerging modernism that 'attempted to shake off the shackles of history'. For Schorske, the development of the *Ringstrasse*, a ring road around the old inner city, served as a powerful metaphor for the museum-like confinement of the past.[124] More recently, geographers such as Ash Amin and Stephen Graham have pointed to the limits of what they call 'synecdoche in new urbanism'. Such an orientation assumes that a small set of exceptional cities can serve as a universal model for all cities, and that cities can be evaluated according to a

---

*Thought, 1820-1940*, Manchester: Manchester University Press, 1985, p. 73; S. Frederick Starr, 'Illusion and Disillusion', in T. R. Johnson (ed.), *New Orleans: A Literary History*, Cambridge: Cambridge University Press, 2019; Mary Gluck, *The Invisible Jewish Budapest: Metropolitan Culture at the Fin de Siècle*, Madison: University of Wisconsin Press, 2016; Grace Ellison, quoted in Davide Deriu, 'A Challenge to the West: British Views of Republican Ankara', in Mohammad Gharipour and Nilay Ozlu (eds.), *The City in the Muslim World: Depictions by Western Travel Writers*, London: Routledge, 2015, p. 283.

[122] See, for example, Richard Sennett, *The Conscience of the Eye: The Design and Social Life of Cities*, London: Faber and Faber, 1991; Lloyd Rodwin and Robert M. Hollister (eds.), *Cities of the Mind: Images and Themes of the City in the Social Sciences*, New York: Plenum Press, 1984; Alexander C. Diener and Joshua Hagen (eds.), *The City as Power: Urban Space, Place, and National Identity*, Lanham: Rowman & Littlefield, 2019; and Ernesto Capello, *City at the Center of the World: Space, History, and Modernity in Quito*, Pittsburgh: University of Pittsburgh Press, 2011. For a reflection on changing understandings of 'urbanity' see Susanne Rau, 'Urbanity (urbanitas, Urbanität, urbanité, urbanità, urbanidad…)', in id. and Jörg Rüpke (eds.), *Religion and Urbanity Online*, Berlin: De Gruyter, 2020. Available HTTP: <https://www.degruyter.com/database/URBREL/entry/urbrel.11276000/html> (accessed 19 March 2021).

[123] See, for example, David Harvey, *Paris, Capital of Modernity*, New York and London: Routledge, 2006; Emma Hart, *Trading Spaces: The Colonial Marketplace and the Foundations of American Capitalism*, Chicago and London: University of Chicago Press, 2019; Miles Ogborn, *Spaces of Modernity: London's Geographies, 1680-1780*, New York: Guilford Press, 1998; Richard Dennis, *Cities in Modernity: Representations and Productions of Metropolitan Space, 1840-1930*, Cambridge: Cambridge University Press, 2008; Leif Jerram, *Streetlife: How Cities Made Modern Europe*, Oxford: Oxford University Press, 2011; Joseph W. Esherick (ed.), *Remaking the Chinese City: Modernity and National Identity, 1900-1950*, Honolulu: University of Hawaii Press, 1999; Su Lin Lewis, *Cities in Motion: Urban Life and Cosmopolitanism in Southeast Asia, 1920–1940*, Cambridge: Cambridge University Press, 2016; Katharina von Ankum, *Women in the Metropolis: Gender and Modernity in Weimar Culture*, Berkeley: University of California Press, 1997; Wen-hsin Yeh, *Shanghai Splendor: Economic Sentiments and the Making of Modern China, 1843-1949*, Berkeley: University of California Press, 2007.

[124] Carl E. Schorske, *Fin-de-Siècle Vienna: Politics and Culture*, New York: Knopf, 1979, pp. xviii, 33; see also Mark D. Steinberg, *Petersburg Fin de Siècle*, New Haven: Yale University Press, 2011.

distinctly Western conception of modernity.[125] Jennifer Robinson's influential work *Ordinary Cities* (2006) traced this tendency through discourses on the city over the past century. Robinson is one of many scholars working to post-colonise urban studies.[126]

Debates over cities as spaces of modernity also have an important gender dimension. This is especially so when city space is coded as public and male, both by contemporaries and scholars.[127] The home, as much as the city, is a place to look for signs of, and responses to, modernity. It thus deserves to be treated as something more than a nostalgic other. As Judy Giles puts it in *The Parlour and the Suburb* (2004), 'when we speak of home […] we are often speaking of something else. That "something else" is linked to our most utopian dreams and thus articulates profound needs and desires that are themselves the products of modernity.'[128]

---

[125] Ash Amin and Stephen Graham, 'The Ordinary City', *Transactions of the Institute of British Geographers* 22, 1997, 411–29.

[126] Jennifer Robinson, *Ordinary Cities: Between Modernity and Development*, London: Routledge, 2006; see also Manish Chalana and Jeffrey Hou (ed.), *Messy Urbanism: Understanding the 'Other' Cities of Asia*, Hong Kong: Hong Kong University Press, 2017; Gyan Prakash and Kevin M. Kruse (eds.), *The Spaces of the Modern City: Imaginaries, Politics, and Everyday Life*, Princeton: Princeton University Press, 2008; Ananya Roy and Nezar AlSayyad, *Urban Informality: Transnational Perspectives from the Middle East, Latin America, and South Asia*, Lanham: Lexington Books, 2004; and the selection of readings in Faranak Miraftab and Neema Kudva, *Cities of the Global South Reader*, Oxford and New York: Routledge, 2014. The appreciation of the role of smaller or 'second' cities can be seen in works such as David Bell and Mark Jayne (eds.), *Small Cities: Urban Experience Beyond the Metropolis*, Oxford and New York: Routledge, 2006; as well as Jens Hanssen, *Fin de Siècle Beirut: The Making of an Ottoman Provincial Capital*, Oxford: Clarendon Press, 2005; and Louise Young, *Beyond the Metropolis: Second Cities and Modern Life in Interwar Japan*, Berkeley: University of California Press, 2013.

[127] See D'Souza and McDonough (eds.), *The Invisible Flâneuse?*; Rita Felski, *The Gender of Modernity*, Cambridge, Mass.: Harvard University Press, 1995; Elizabeth Wilson, *The Sphinx in the City: Urban Life, the Control of Disorder, and Women*, Berkeley: University of California Press, 1992; Deborah L. Parsons, *Streetwalking the Metropolis: Women, the City and Modernity*, Oxford: Oxford University Press, 2000; Kristine B. Miranne and Alma H. Young (eds.), *Gendering the City: Women, Boundaries, and Visions of Urban Life*, Lanham: Rowman & Littlefield, 2000; Alys Eve Weinbaum et al. (eds.), *The Modern Girl Around the World: Consumption, Modernity, and Globalization*, Durham: Duke University Press, 2008; Lin Foxhall and Gabriele Neher (eds.), *Gender and the City before Modernity*, Malden, Mass.: John Wiley & Sons, 2013; see also Sarah Deutsch, *Women and the City: Gender, Space, and Power in Boston, 1870-1940*, New York: Oxford University Press, 2000; as well as the chapter by Sarah Deutsch in Bavaj, Lawson and Struck (eds.), *Doing Spatial History*.

[128] Judy Giles, *The Parlour and the Suburb: Domestic Identities, Class, Femininity and Modernity*, Oxford: Berg, 2004; see also Jordan Sand, *House and Home in Modern Japan: Reforming Everyday Life 1880-1930*, Cambridge, Mass.: Harvard University Press, 2003; Elizabeth LaCouture, *Dwelling in the World: Family, House, and Home in Tianjin, China, 1860–1960*, New York: Columbia University Press, 2021; Ruth Schwartz Cowan, *More Work for Mother: The Ironies of Household Technology from the Open Hearth to the Microwave*, New York: Basic Books, 1983.

Both the city and the home have long been the spaces in which we have dreamed these utopian dreams. In modern times, Ebenezer Howard's 'Garden City' (1898), the holistic perspectives on urban planning of Patrick Geddes around the turn of the century, Le Corbusier's 'Radiant City' (1930), as well as socialist realism, have all had a deep impact on utopian spatial ambitions for reordering human life in the city. Other writers have sounded warning calls about the limits of top-down planning in the urban environment. Notable in this respect was *The Death and Life of Great American Cities* (1961) by writer and architectural critic Jane Jacobs.[129] At the scale of mass housing and the home, architects, housewives, and governments have all struggled for predominant control over the form, presentation, and spatial ordering of our most intimate places.[130]

Utopian attempts to reorder space in both city and home come into closest contact with each other in accounts of the modern residential suburb. This can be seen in, for example, the development of Tokyo's planned suburb of Den'en Chōfu in the 1920s. Based in part on ideas of the Garden City, the project's

---

[129] Jane Jacobs, *The Death and Life of Great American Cities*, New York: Random House, 1961; see Peter Hall, *Cities of Tomorrow: An Intellectual History of Urban Planning and Design since 1880*, 4th ed., Malden, Mass.: Wiley & Sons, 2014; Stanley Buder, *Visionaries and Planners: The Garden City Movement and the Modern Community*, Oxford: Oxford University Press, 1990; Margaret Crawford, *Building the Workingman's Paradise: The Design of American Company Towns*, London: Verso, 1995; John R. Gold, *The Experience of Modernism: Modern Architects and the Future City, 1928-53*, London: E & FN Spon, 1997. Some case study examples include Crowley and Reid (eds.), *Socialist Spaces*; Kenny Cupers, *The Social Project: Housing Postwar France*, Minneapolis: University of Minnesota Press, 2014; Marija Drėmaitė, *Baltic Modernism: Architecture and Housing in Soviet Lithuania*, Berlin: DOM Publishers, 2017; Till Großmann and Philipp Nielsen (eds.), *Architecture, Democracy, and Emotions: The Politics of Feeling since 1945*, London and New York: Routledge, 2019; Steven E. Harris, *Communism on Tomorrow Street: Mass Housing and Everyday Life after Stalin*, Washington DC: Woodrow Wilson Center Press, 2013; Owen Hatherley, *Landscapes of Communism: A History through Buildings*, London: Allen Lane, 2015; Katherine Lebow, *Unfinished Utopia: Nowa Huta, Stalinism, and Polish Society, 1949–56*, Ithaca: Cornell University Press, 2013; Brigitte Le Normand, *Designing Tito's Capital: Urban Planning, Modernism, and Socialism*, Pittsburgh: University of Pittsburgh Press, 2014; Otto Saumarez Smith, *Boom Cities: Architect Planners and the Politics of Radical Urban Renewal in 1960s Britain*, Oxford: Oxford University Press, 2019; Karl Schlögel, *Moscow 1937*, Cambridge: Polity, 2012, German 2008; Łukasz Stanek, *Architecture in Global Socialism: Eastern Europe, West Africa, and the Middle East in the Cold War*, Princeton: Princeton University Press, 2020.

[130] Nicole Rudolph, "'Who Should Be the Author of a Dwelling?'": Architects versus Housewives in 1950s France', in Adler and Hamilton, *Homes and Homecomings*, pp. 87-105; see also Dolores Hayden, *The Grand Domestic Revolution: A History of Feminist Designs for American Homes, Neighborhoods, and Cities*, Cambridge, Mass. and London: MIT Press, 1981; id., *Redesigning the American Dream: The Future of Housing, Work, and Family Life*, New York: W.W. Norton, 1984; Gwendolyn Wright, *Moralism and the Model Home: Domestic Architecture and Cultural Conflict in Chicago, 1873-1913*, Chicago and London: University of Chicago Press, 1980.

hybrid Western-Japanese houses promised a modern 'cultured' life. As Jordan Sand observed in his excellent study *House and Home in Modern Japan* (2003), 'the exotic occident sustained a dreamscape'.[131]

Above all, as we will see with the closer examination of one example below, cities are highly contested spaces. In these spaces, overt planning, economic inequalities, and lived practices interact in complex ways. Race and ethnicity both have a powerful impact on the spatial ordering of cities. Indeed, these factors have been explored in depth by scholars from multiple disciplines.[132] Moreover, space and place in the city have frequently been foregrounded in histories of sexuality. A pathbreaking study in this respect was George Chauncey's *Gay New York* (1995). This self-consciously spatial historical work set itself the task of reconstructing the 'sexual topography of the gay world'.[133]

---

[131] Sand, *House and Home in Modern Japan*, p. 237; see also Ken Tadashi Oshima, 'Denenchōfu: Building the Garden City in Japan', *Journal of the Society of Architectural Historians* 55/2, 1996, 140–51; for more on suburbs, see Nikhil Rao, *House, but No Garden: Apartment Living in Bombay's Suburbs, 1898-1964*, Minneapolis: University of Minnesota Press, 2013; Robert Fishman, *Bourgeois Utopias: The Rise and Fall Of Suburbia*, New York: Basic Books, 1987; Kenneth T. Jackson, *Crabgrass Frontier: The Suburbanization of the United States*, New York: Oxford University Press, 1985; Dolores Hayden, *Building Suburbia: Green Fields and Urban Growth, 1820-2000*, New York: Pantheon Books, 2003; and the interdisciplinary collection of documents and essays in Becky M. Nicolaides and Andrew Wiese (eds.), *The Suburb Reader*, New York and London: Routledge, 2006; see also Becky M. Nicolaides, *My Blue Heaven: Life and Politics in the Working-Class Suburbs of Los Angeles, 1920-1965*, Chicago and London: University of Chicago Press, 2002; Andrew Wiese, *Places of Their Own: African American Suburbanization in the Twentieth Century*, Chicago and London: University of Chicago Press, 2004; Timothy P. Fong, *The First Suburban Chinatown: The Remaking of Monterey Park, California*, Philadelphia: Temple University Press, 1994.

[132] The literature on this is vast. See here Carl H. Nightingale, *Segregation: A Global History of Divided Cities*, Chicago and London: University of Chicago Press, 2012; Janet L. Abu-Lughod, *Rabat: Urban Apartheid in Morocco*, Princeton: Princeton University Press, 1980; Arnold R. Hirsch, *Making the Second Ghetto: Race and Housing in Chicago, 1940-1960*, Cambridge: Cambridge University Press, 1983; Nayan Shah, *Contagious Divides: Epidemics and Race in San Francisco's Chinatown*, Berkeley: University of California Press, 2001; Emily Honig, *Creating Chinese Ethnicity: Subei People in Shanghai, 1850-1980*, New Haven: Yale University Press, 1992; Dana E. Katz, *The Jewish Ghetto and the Visual Imagination of Early Modern Venice*, Cambridge: Cambridge University Press, 2017.

[133] George Chauncey, *Gay New York: Gender, Urban Culture, and the Making of the Gay Male World, 1890-1940*, New York: Basic Books, 1994, p. 23; see also David Higgs (ed.), *Queer Sites: Gay Urban Histories since 1600*, London: Routledge, 1999; Matt Houlbrook, *Queer London: Perils and Pleasures in the Sexual Metropolis, 1918-1957*, Chicago: University of Chicago Press, 2005; Simon Avery and Katherine M. Graham, (eds.), *Sex, Time and Place: Queer Histories of London, c.1850 to the Present*, London: Bloomsbury, 2016; Christina B. Hanhardt, *Safe Space: Gay Neighborhood History and the Politics of Violence*, Durham: Duke University Press, 2013; Nan Alamilla Boyd, *Wide-Open Town: A History of Queer San Francisco to 1965*, Berkeley: University of California Press, 2003; Jennifer V. Evans and Matt Cook (eds.), *Queer Cities, Queer Cultures: Europe since 1945*, London: Bloomsbury, 2014; Anita Kurimay, *Queer Budapest, 1873-1961*, Chicago and London: University of Chicago Press, 2020.

Historical scholarship on cities and imperialism has justifiably retained a strong central focus on debates around economic development and the interaction of empire and capitalism. This can be seen in, for example, the works of the sociologist Anthony D. King.[134] However, studies of cities and empire also includes some of the most innovative engagements with space that unite economic, cultural and intellectual realms. This includes work on the ways in which the empire was represented spatially within imperial metropoles, to explorations of the vast gap between the colonial fantasies of urban planners and the social realities of the cities they sought to reorder, such as we see in Garth Andrew Myers' *Verandahs of Power* (2003) or William Cunningham Bissell's *Urban Design, Chaos, and Colonial Power in Zanzibar* (2011).[135]

Swati Chattopadhyay's self-described spatial history *Representing Calcutta* (2005) compares British and Bengali 'bids for spatial mastery' in their representations of the city.[136] *Representing Calcutta,* much like work by Bissell on Zanzibar, shows how little congruence there was between, on the one hand, colonial claims for a 'white' town in Calcutta and, on the other, the reality of a more complex racialised spatial order. Chattopadhyay takes this a step further, however. In his book, we meet newly arrived, and confused, British nationals who quickly discovered that, while buildings in 'their' part of the city appeared comfortingly Western from the exterior, 'on closer inspection the interior of the houses functioned according to different rules.'[137]

Todd A. Henry's *Assimilating Seoul* (2014) and Joseph R. Allen's *Taipei: City of Displacements* (2012) offer further excellent examples of the potentials of

---

[134] See, for example, Anthony D. King, *Colonial Urban Development: Culture, Social Power and Environment,* London: Routledge, 1976; id., *Urbanism, Colonialism, and the World-Economy: Cultural and Spatial Foundations of the World Urban System,* Oxford: Routledge, 1990. Compare these works with his very different cultural history of the bungalow: *The Bungalow: The Production of a Global Culture,* London: Routledge, 1984.

[135] Garth Andrew Myers, *Verandahs of Power: Colonialism and Space in Urban Africa,* Syracuse: Syracuse University Press, 2003; William Cunningham Bissell, *Urban Design, Chaos, and Colonial Power in Zanzibar,* Bloomington: Indiana University Press, 2011; for an example of exploring imperial spaces in the metropoles, see Felix Driver and David Gilbert (eds.), *Imperial Cities: Landscape, Display and Identity,* Manchester: Manchester University Press, 1999; see also Stephen Legg, *Spaces of Colonialism: Delhi's Urban Governmentalities,* Oxford: Blackwell, 2007; Jay Kinsbruner, *The Colonial Spanish-American City: Urban Life in the Age of Atlantic Capitalism,* Austin: University of Texas Press, 2005; Robert K. Home, *Of Planting and Planning: The Making of British Colonial Cities,* London: E & FN Spon, 1997; and the superb article by Jeremy E. Taylor, 'The Bund: Littoral Space of Empire in the Treaty Ports of East Asia', *Social History* 27/2, 2002, 125–42.

[136] Swati Chattopadhyay, *Representing Calcutta: Modernity, Nationalism, and the Colonial Uncanny,* London: Routledge, 2005.

[137] Ibid., p. 92.

spatial history in exploring cities that spent decades under Japanese colonial rule. Allen uses the full range of meanings implied by the idea of 'displacement' to explore the symbolic value, erasure and contradictory representations of Taiwanese history. In doing so, he draws on maps, photographs, museum exhibits, urban morphology, statues, and the many layers of Taipei Park.[138] Henry's study of the 'colonial politics of place-making' makes use of several case studies in order to show how the Japanese attempted to convert a royal/imperial Korean city into a Japanese colonial capital. These include, for example, the use of a newly built Korea Shrine Shintō complex on the city's Namsan mountain in order to spiritually assimilate the city's subjects; the spatial politics surrounding the conversion of the former Korean royal palace grounds for a new Government-General building; and the use of the grounds to host two major expositions depicting colonial achievements.[139] In both cases, Henry and Allen combine rich empirical analysis of the materiality of locales with careful attention to the differing spatial perspectives of the coloniser and the colonised.

## Contesting Space in Colonial Singapore

The geographer Brenda Yeoh's *Contesting Space in Colonial Singapore: Power Relations and the Urban Built Environment* (1996) is a model example of a spatial history which successfully incorporates both a broader colonial urban environment and its close interconnections to the contested politics of everyday domestic spaces. [140] Yeoh focuses on conflict, negotiation, and dialogue in a history of interactions between two principal entities: the Municipal Authority of Singapore and the city's diverse Asian communities. The latter have lived in Singapore since 1822, with the creation of a plan for the city by Stamford Raffles, its British founder. This plan included a racialised

---

[138] Joseph R. Allen, *Taipei: City of Displacements*, Seattle and London: University of Washington Press, 2012.

[139] Todd A. Henry, *Assimilating Seoul: Japanese Rule and the Politics of Public Space in Colonial Korea, 1910–1945*, Berkeley: University of California Press, 2014, p. 4. The much longer history of urban spaces in East Asia is a rich field. Two strong examples from the case of China include Paul Wheatley, *The Pivot of the Four Quarters: A Preliminary Enquiry into the Origins and Character of the Ancient Chinese City*, Edinburgh: Edinburgh University Press, 1971; and Nancy Shatzman Steinhardt, *Chinese Imperial City Planning*, Honolulu: University of Hawaii Press, 1990.

[140] Brenda S. A. Yeoh, *Contesting Space in Colonial Singapore: Power Relations and the Urban Built Environment*, Singapore: NUS Press, 2003, first published 1996, p. 10.

spatial vision of a European town combined with Chinese, Malay, and Indian districts.[141]

Yeoh argues that the evolving colonial administration's sanitary controls were the main tool for controlling the city's numerous 'principal spatial variables'. These included the extent of the state's gaze into streets and homes, or their very structure, spacing, and patterns of practice.[142] Several chapters in the book are dedicated to these unfolding ambitions. In each case, Yeoh traces the responses of the Asian communities in the city as well as, usually, the resulting frustrations and failure of the municipal government's goals. Sanitary control was just as much at the heart of municipal reforms in Europe as in colonial settings. In Singapore, as with many other colonial cities, overcrowding and insanitary conditions were attributed to the presumed 'intrinsic racial peculiarities' of the Asian communities – something which parallels similar claims about racial and ethnic minorities in imperial metropoles as well. That such issues might be produced by economic inequality or the deliberate policies of the colonial administration was not, of course, usually a dominant theme in discussion, at least on the side of the colonisers.

Sanitary inspectors reached into the home to oppose the very spatial distribution of occupants within buildings by waging a war against cubicle subdivisions. This entailed the use of simple and often temporary internal dividers in order to multiply internal spaces for tenants in a rapidly growing city.[143] In their efforts to create new back lanes between densely packed back-to-back houses, municipal policies compounded house scarcity without offering new housing provisions, while simultaneously transforming private into public spaces.[144] Even as they attacked night soil collection and the use of the amassed human excreta as fertilizer in urban gardens, the municipal government long delayed efforts to offer an alternative sewage infrastructure. This policy was justified by vague suggestions that these modern conveniences were ill-suited to the diverse toilet practices of Asian populations, despite evidence of its smooth introduction on individual streets.[145]

---

[141] Ibid., p. 40; for a critique of overemphasising these origin moments for colonial cities, see Chattopadhyay *Representing Calcutta*, p. 10.

[142] Yeoh, *Contesting Space*, p. 82.

[143] Ibid., pp. 146-8.

[144] Ibid., pp. 148-57.

[145] Ibid., chapter 5.

Yeoh also shows how the municipal government's attempts to create a 'landscape of clarity'[146] in the city were consistently frustrated. Efforts to make the city legible ranged from using the power of naming and keeping it alive to the demands of capital, to the expulsion of inalienable sacred spaces from the heart of the city. Two regimes of naming came to co-exist. One took the form of official municipal names, while a second, competing set of names was used by the city's Asian communities. These systems evinced 'little direct correspondence' and represented starkly different ways of signifying urban space. Western municipal names drew on famous personages and nostalgic references to home. Conversely, Chinese street nomenclature was 'strongly anchored to local features, symbols, and activities which formed a significant part of quotidian experience.'[147]

Among these campaigns, perhaps the most spatially interesting case is that of the verandahs. These were covered 'five-foot-ways' for passage found along the front of buildings throughout the city. From the founding of Singapore, the verandahs were designed to be reserved spaces for public circulation. Yeoh explores their rich complexity in the daily life of the city: they were 'as much a place – the locus of economic, communal, and occasionally clandestine activities – as a passage.'[148] Municipal officials deplored the 'usurpers of the verandah space', or the 'obstructionists', as those who impeded free movement. In 1888, however, attempts to clear them were met with riots.[149]

Michel de Certeau famously contrasted the 'practised place' and 'pedestrian speech acts' of 'walkers' who create their own 'mobile organicity' in a city with the top-down, rationalised conceptual view of city planners. Yeoh's book, however, provides us with an illuminating example of how more immobile varieties of spatial appropriation could also thwart the designs of urban planners.[150]

---

[146] Ibid., p. 215.

[147] Ibid., p. 231.

[148] Ibid., p. 247.

[149] Ibid., p. 250.

[150] De Certeau, *The Practice of Everyday Life*, pp. 97-9.

# 4 Social Space and Political Protest

'There is a politics of space because space is political'. This statement was written by Henri Lefebvre in 1970. It came in the wake of the student protests of May 1968, and a few years before the publication of *The Production of Space* (1974/91), the book that would later gain him posthumous fame.[151] The organisation, design and use of space – especially public space – is undoubtedly a matter of political significance. It is thus intensely political. Questions of spatial organisation, co-produced through historically evolving 'modes of production' (Karl Marx), conceptions of architecture and planning, as well as place-making practices, tend to be fiercely contested. Who has access to public space? Who, or what, decides where people live? Whose (hi)stories are represented? Which relations to 'broader political imaginaries' are made visible? Who 'owns' the city? These and similar questions have been the subject of debate for decades. Interventions range from Jane Jacobs' *The Death and Life of Great American Cities* (1961), Lefebvre's *The Right to the City* (1968) and David Harvey's *Social Justice and the City* (1973), to more recent publications such as Dolores Hayden's *The Power of Place* (1995) and David Featherstone's *Resistance, Space and Political Identities* (2008).[152]

The broad contours of Lefebvre's triadic approach to space are outlined in the introduction to *Doing Spatial History*, and need not be rehashed here. That said, it is important to note Lefebvre's emphasis on both a critique of modern urbanism, and on the utopia of dialectically produced spaces of resistance, difference, and liberation.[153] More specifically, the main focus for this section of the guide is Lefebvre's insight into space as 'the ultimate locus and medium of struggle', as Stuart Elden has put it.[154] This insight, like Lefebvre's work

---

[151] Henri Lefebvre, 'Reflections on the Politics of Space' (1970), in id., *State, Space, World: Selected Essays*, eds. Neil Brenner and Stuart Elden, Minneapolis: University of Minnesota Press, 2009, pp. 167-84, here p. 174.

[152] Jacobs, *Great American Cities*; Henri Lefebvre, *Writings on Cities*, trans. Eleonore Kofman and Elizabeth Lebas, Oxford: Blackwell, 1996; Harvey, *Social Justice and the City*; Dolores Hayden, *The Power of Place: Urban Landscapes as Public History*, Cambridge, Mass. and London: MIT Press, 1995; David Featherstone, *Resistance, Space and Political Identities: The Making of Counter-Global Networks*, Oxford: Wiley-Blackwell, 2008. For the quote 'broader political imaginaries' see David Featherstone, 'Towards the Relational Construction of Militant Particularisms: Or Why the Geographies of Past Struggles Matter for Resistance to Neoliberal Globalisation', *Antipode* 37, 2005, 250-71, here 252.

[153] Henri Lefebvre, *The Urban Revolution*, Minneapolis: University of Minnesota Press, 2003, French 1970.

[154] Stuart Elden, 'There is a Politics of Space because Space is Political: Henri Lefebvre and the

49

more generally, has proven inspirational to many scholars working on social space and political protest.

An early example of a work steeped in Lefebvrean thought is *The Emergence of Social Space* (1988), an imaginative study of French poet Arthur Rimbaud and the 1871 Paris Commune written by literary scholar Kristin Ross.[155] When writing this book, Ross was also influenced by Fredric Jameson's spatial ventures, some of which are surveyed in the introduction to *Doing Spatial History*. Jameson's work had resulted in the extension of an invitation to Lefebvre to spend time as a scholar in residence at the University of California at Santa Cruz in 1983. Ross was teaching at this institution at precisely this point in time. She took the opportunity to conduct an interview with Lefebvre, which focused on the topic of former Situationists.[156] Ross was thus thoroughly inspired by various 'afterlives' of May 1968.[157] Her study offers numerous suggestive readings of Rimbaud's poetry by placing it, via a 'synchronic history', in a variety of historical contexts. These range from the subversive place-making strategies of Paris Communards to the formation of the discipline of geography, as well as its anarchist Communard dissident Élisée Reclus, to the colonial spaces of the French empire.[158]

For example, Ross interprets the Communards' toppling of the Vendôme Column, symbol of the exploits of Napoleon's army, as a spatially performative act of 'horizontalizing' social hierarchies. Through this and other acts of transgression, the Communards – among them many women – reshaped both physical and social space. They fought over questions of ownership and the everyday use of streets, squares, and neighbourhoods, opposing the 'social

---

Production of Space', *Radical Philosophy Review* 10, 2007, 101-16, here 107; see also Neil Brenner and Stuart Elden, 'State, Space, World: Lefebvre and the Survival of Capitalism', in Lefebvre, *State, Space, World*, pp. 1-48, here esp. pp. 32-3.

[155] Kristin Ross, *The Emergence of Social Space: Rimbaud and the Paris Commune*, London: Verso, 1988.

[156] Kristin Ross, 'Lefebvre on Situationists: An Interview', *October* 79, Winter 1997, 69-83.

[157] This source of inspiration is explicitly acknowledged in Ross, *Emergence of Social Space*, pp. 8-9, and has also become the subject of one of her later books: Kristin Ross, *May '68 and Its Afterlives*, Chicago and London: University of Chicago Press, 2002.

[158] Ross, *Emergence of Social Space*, p. 10 ('synchronic history'). As Terry Eagleton puts it in his foreword to the book, Ross sees 'the very language of the poems alive with electric currents and shocking conjunctures that spring from a more-than-literary source'. 'Political history inscribes itself in the very force fields of [Rimbaud's] texts, between the lines and within the rhythms'. Terry Eagleton, 'Foreword', in Ross, *Emergence of Social Space*, pp. vi-xiv, here pp. x-xi. On Reclus, see now also Federico Ferretti, '"They Have the Right to Throw us Out": Élisée Reclus' *Nouvelle Géographie Universelle*', *Antipode* 45, 2013, 1337-55; Pascale Siegrist, 'Cosmopolis and Community: Élisée Reclus and Pëtr Kropotkin on Spatial and Moral Unity, 1870s to 1900s', *Global Intellectual History*, September 2020.

classification and policing of everyday life' by *gendarme, concierge* and other regulating forces of social control.

Crucially, Ross sees the spontaneously eruptive actions of the Communards as evidence of the fact that they were agreeably 'out of sync' with any notions of a 'unilinear' teleological 'Highway of History' – Marxist or otherwise. She also detects, in Rimbaud's oppositional vernacular language, an anti-narrative, anti-progressivist, vagabondage-like spatiality. Ross contends that both Rimbaud and the Communards drew on 'the elements or terrain of the dominant social order to one's own ends, for a transformed purpose'. This epitomises what Lefebvre called 'lived space', and his fellow Situationists referred to as *détournement.*[159]

In recent decades, political protest and popular radicalism have been the subject of much spatially attuned research in modern British history.[160] Laura Forster, for example, has traced exiled Communards to London. She has carefully examined the exchange of political ideas that occurred there through a mapping of the meeting places of London's radical and exile communities. These ranged from pubs and shops to clubs and reading rooms. 'It matters', she states, '*where* people meet and *where* discussions take place', not least because they 'respond to the subtle atmospheres that make a place variously inviting, hostile, affecting, stirring, or fearsome. Generating spaces of intellectual kinship, comradery, and intimacy, therefore, is shaped by both people *and* place.'[161]

Similarly, Christina Parolin has focused on sites of popular radicalism in London during the early nineteenth century, placing particular emphasis on prisons, taverns, and the radical theatre 'Rotunda'. This last location was also used by female activists to shape radical political culture. The Crown and

---

[159] Ross, *Emergence of Social Space*, pp. 22, 25, 42; see also Kristin Ross, *Communal Luxury: The Political Imaginary of the Paris Commune*, London and New York: Verso, 2015; as well as Harvey, *Paris, Capital of Modernity*; Peter Starr, *Commemorating Trauma: The Paris Commune and Its Cultural Aftermath*, New York: Fordham University Press, 2006. To capture the 'proliferation of geographic names' in Rimbaud's later poetry, she uses, with no explicit recourse to Paul Carter, the term 'spatial history'. Ibid., pp. 75, 88. For an example of a later study in literary history that explicitly draws on the methodology of both Kristin Ross and Paul Carter, see Andrew Thacker, *Moving through Modernity: Space and Geography in Modernism*, Manchester: Manchester University Press, 2003, here esp. p. 5; see also, in this context, Phillip E. Wegner, *Imaginary Communities: Utopia, the Nation, and the Spatial Histories of Modernity*, Berkeley: University of California Press, 2002.

[160] For a recent overview see Hannah Awcock, 'New Protest History: Exploring the Historical Geographies and Geographical Histories of Resistance through Gender, Practice, and Materiality', *Geography Compass* 14/6, 2020, 1-10.

[161] Laura C. Forster, 'The Paris Commune in London and the Spatial History of Ideas, 1871-1900', *The Historical Journal* 62, 2019, 1021-44, here p. 1026 (original emphasis).

Anchor tavern had been a liberal-Whig headquarters. However, it was gradually transformed into a 'radical space' – a process which is captured in Parolin's book through both social practice and visual representation (caricature and graphic satire).[162]

Parolin primarily follows in the footsteps here of James Epstein. In 1999, Epstein published a stimulating article in *Social History* titled 'Spatial Practices/Democratic Vistas'. This contribution sought to incorporate analytical insights from spatially attentive work into the historiography on British popular radicalism. Epstein drew on Henri Lefebvre, Kristin Ross and Paul Carter, as well as Brenda Yeoh's *Contesting Space* and Mary Poovey's Lefebvrean analysis of 'abstract space' and 'social body' in early- and mid-nineteenth-century British social discourse. 'In large part', Epstein argued, 'the history of popular radicalism can […] be written as a contest to gain access to and to appropriate sites of assembly and expression, to produce, at least potentially, a "plebeian counter-public sphere"'.[163]

In this vein, the past two decades have seen the publication of myriad studies on radicalism and protest, both urban and rural, which have drawn inspiration from Lefebvre or other variants of spatial theory. These range from work on social protest in the Scottish Highlands and contestations of public space in modern Belfast to studies on German anarchists in turn-of-the-century New York, as well as squatters in 1980s Berlin. They also encompass explorations of the 1919 student protest at Peking University, the Tiananmen Square protests of 1989, and the anti-Vietnam war protests in Tokyo at Shinjuku Station's underground 'plaza' in 1968. These contributions bear out

---

[162] Christina Parolin, *Radical Spaces: Venues of Popular Politics in London, 1790-c.1845*, Canberra: ANU Press, 2010, p. 175; see also, in this context, Hannah Awcock, 'The Geographies of Protest and Public Space in Mid-Nineteenth-Century London: The Hyde Park Railings Affair', *Historical Geography* 47, 2019, 194-217; as well as the 'space syntax'-based analysis by Sam Griffiths and Katrina Navickas, 'The Micro-Geography of Political Meeting Places in Manchester and Sheffield, c.1780-1850', in Alida Clemente, Dag Lindström and Jon Stobart (eds.), *Micro-Geographies of the Western City, c.1750-1900*, London: Routledge, 2020, pp. 181-202; see also the chapter by Kate Ferris in Bavaj, Lawson and Struck (eds.), *Doing Spatial History*.

[163] James Epstein, 'Spatial Practices/Democratic Vistas', *Social History* 24, 1999, 294-310, here 301 (a slightly revised version of this article has been published in id., *In Practice: Studies in the Language and Culture of Popular Politics in Modern Britain*, Stanford: Stanford University Press, 2003, pp. 106-25); see also Mary Poovey, *Making a Social Body: British Cultural Formation, 1830-1864*, Chicago and London: University of Chicago Press, 1995, pp. 25-54 ('The Production of Abstract Space').

what William H. Sewell described, in 2001, as the 'importance of spatial structure in shaping protest' and the significance of spatial agency in producing 'new spatial structures, meanings, and routines'.[164]

## Protest and the Politics of Space and Place

Social space and political protest are also at the heart of Katrina Navickas' exemplary study on English radicalism from the late eighteenth to the mid nineteenth centuries. It is not an exaggeration to describe this book as the spatial history equivalent of E.P. Thompson's *The Making of the English Working Class* (1963). Navickas – a member of the Centre for Regional and Local History at the University of Hertfordshire – examines the contestation of public space through the streetscapes of the industrial North. This is, she writes at the outset of her book, 'a narrative of the closing down of public space' to people who were fighting for democracy.[165] In the book's three sections, she focuses on urban 'spaces of exclusion', 'spaces of the body politic', and rural spaces of protest.

Navickas' study throws into sharp relief the importance of place and space for the manifestation of political protest. It vividly illustrates how radicalism both shaped and was shaped by the restricted spaces available. It also shows how, in and through those spaces, political demands and aspirations were

---

[164] William H. Sewell, Jr., 'Space in Contentious Politics', in Ronald R. Aminzade et al. (eds.), *Silence and Voice in the Study of Contentious Politics*, Cambridge: Cambridge University Press, 2001, pp. 51-88, here pp. 71, 88; see, for example, Iain J.M. Robertson, *Landscapes of Protest in the Scottish Highlands after 1914*, London: Routledge, 2013, esp. pp. 195-216; Dominic Bryan and S.J. Connolly (with John Nagle), *Civic Identity and Public Space. Belfast since 1870*, Manchester: Manchester University Press, 2019, esp. pp. 10-13; Georgina Laragy, Olwen Purdue and Jonathan Jeffrey Wright (eds.), *Urban Spaces in Nineteenth-Century Ireland*, Liverpool: Liverpool University Press, 2018, esp. the introduction by Olwen Purdue and Jonathan Jeffrey Wright, pp. 1-12, here pp. 4-6; Tom Goyens, 'Social Space and the Practice of Anarchist History', *Rethinking History* 13, 2009, 439-57; Alexander Vasudevan, *Metropolitan Preoccupations: The Spatial Politics of Squatting in Berlin*, Malden, Mass.: John Wiley & Sons, 2015; Fabio Lanza, *Behind the Gate: Inventing Students in Beijing*, New York: Columbia University Press, 2010; Wu Hung, *Remaking Beijing: Tiananmen Square and the Creation of a Political Space*, London: Reaktion, 2005; Jordan Sand, *Tokyo Vernacular: Common Spaces, Local Histories, Found Objects*, Berkeley: University of California Press, 2013, esp. chapter 1; see also Timothy Scott Brown, *West Germany and the Global Sixties: The Anti-Authoritarian Revolt, 1962-1978*, Cambridge: Cambridge University Press, 2015, pp. 21-78 ('Space'); Simon Gunn and Robert J. Morris (eds.), *Identities in Space: Contested Terrains in the Western City since 1850*, Aldershot: Ashgate, 2001; Mark Jones, 'The Crowd in the German November Revolution 1918', in Klaus Weinhauer, Anthony McElligott and Kirsten Heinsohn (eds.), *Germany 1916-23: A Revolution in Context*, Bielefeld: transcript, 2015, pp. 37-57; Molly Loberg, *The Struggle for the Streets of Berlin: Politics, Consumption, and Urban Space, 1914-1945*, Cambridge: Cambridge University Press, 2018.

[165] Katrina Navickas, *Protest and the Politics of Space and Place, 1789-1848*, Manchester: Manchester University Press, 2016, p. 14.

articulated via speech and song, but also through silence (as in repurposed funeral processions). Navickas illustrates the process by which reformist groups first shifted their activities from private dwellings to the pub – until they were ostracized by loyalist elites. This forced them to switch to urban scrubland, warehouse backrooms, abandoned factory attics, as well as the moorlands as 'spaces of making do'. These groups mixed 'the everyday with the political', transforming the sites they used into new spaces, imbued with popular political associations.[166]

Navickas also follows radicals in their contestations of conventional practices within spaces of established authority, from workhouses to hospitals and parish vestries. These become attempts to obtain representation in the local body politic. Her book depicts members of the Chartist movement during the 1830s and 1840s constructing their own political spaces, such as halls of science. These served a range of educational, recreational, economic and political purposes. Particularly illuminating, moreover, is a vignette-style case study comparing processions of protest in two hubs of Northern radicalism. In Leeds, protesters aimed to undermine the intended symbolic meanings of civic and patriotic processions of the official calendar by reappropriating their routes. In Manchester, meanwhile, they carved out their own processional geographies, traversing the 'martyred ground' of St Peter's Field, the site of the infamous 'Peterloo massacre' of 1819. Indeed, protesters pointedly passed through working-class districts that loyalists avoided at all costs.[167]

In venturing out to rural spaces of protest, Navickas also engages with radicalism in the countryside. This was grounded in 'a deep attachment to the land and its customs and connections', and it combined urban romanticisations of the rural idyll with the more down-to-earth 'taskscape' of agricultural labourers.[168] The book gives particular prominence to the moorlands, which played host to a wide variety of political spectacles, from military manoeuvres and Chartist 'monster meetings' to torchlit processions. A fascinating concluding chapter charts a battle for spatial supremacy in the narrow cobbled streets of small 'neighbourhood' towns and villages, where local radicals used their superior 'street wisdom' to outwit the military forces sent to suppress them. This created an 'urban battlefield', where the weapons of war were, ironically enough, the very same cobblestones introduced by the authorities to

---

[166] Ibid., p. 59.

[167] Ibid., p. 180.

[168] Ibid., pp. 224, 248.

'improve' urban streetscapes.[169] Nothing could more starkly demonstrate the fact that these urban and rural spaces were much more than merely passive backdrops for political powerplay. Certainly, these conflicts were closely connected to the symbolic appropriations of the places where they occurred. More than this, however, these conflicts depended on the ascribed physical qualities and the very materiality of these places.

---

[169] Ibid., pp. 285-6.

# 5 Spaces of Knowledge

How and to what extent do space and place influence the production of scientific knowledge, the process of its dissemination, and the establishment of what constitutes 'truth' and 'scientific fact'? To what extent do local circumstances and geographical contingencies play a role in what constitutes knowledge and what counts as scientific fact? Space, location, and place have long been denied any central importance in studies of the production of scientific knowledge. Science, facts, and truth were deemed to be neutral vis-à-vis their site of production and consumption. Since the 1980s, however, this view has come under intense scrutiny.

In 2005, David Livingstone, professor of geography and intellectual history at the Queen's University of Belfast, asserted that science studies were undergoing a 'geographical turn'.[170] In fact, a 'spatial turn' in the history of science had been well under way by then.[171] Scholars had been turning towards the specific sites and contexts in which science was produced – concrete localities as well as territorialities (in the case of open field work). Such spatial dimensions had to be taken into account in the reconstruction of the making of knowledge and the establishment of scientific facts.

Historians of the Enlightenment such as Dorinda Outram and Jan Golinski have pointed to the emergence of new spatial settings of knowledge production during the eighteenth century. Taking inspiration from Jürgen Habermas' work

---

[170] David N. Livingstone, 'Science, Text and Space: Thoughts on the Geography of Reading', *Transactions of the Institute of British Geographers* 30, 2005, 391-401; see also Diarmid A. Finnegan, 'The Spatial Turn: Geographical Approaches in the History of Science', *Journal of the History of Biology* 41, 2008, 369-88; Simon Naylor, 'Historical Geographies of Science: Places, Contexts, Cartographies', *The British Journal for the History of Science* 38, 2005, 1-12; Richard C. Powell, 'Geographies of Science: Histories, Localities, Practices, Futures', *Progress in Human Geography* 31, 2007, 309-29; Pascal Schillings and Alexander van Wickeren, 'Towards a Material and Spatial History of Knowledge Production', *Historical Social Research* 40, 2015, 203-18; as well as Christian Jacob, *Qu'est-ce qu'un lieu de savoir?*, Marseille: Open Edition Press, 2014; id. (ed.), *Lieux de Savoir. Vol. 1: Espaces et Communités*, Paris: Albin Michel, 2007; Hans-Jörg Rheinberger, Michael Hagner and Bettina Wahrig-Schmidt (eds.), *Räume des Wissens: Repräsentation, Codierung, Spur*, Berlin: Akademie Verlag, 1997. The book series *Knowledge and Space* (Springer) was launched in 2008, first edited by Peter Meusburger (vols. 1-13, 2008-18), and since 2019 by Johannes Glückler (vols. 14-17, 2019-21).

[171] See, for instance, the earlier articles by David N. Livingstone, 'The History of Science and the History of Geography: Interactions and Implications', *History of Science* 22, 1984, 271-302; id., 'The Spaces of Knowledge: Contributions Towards a Historical Geography of Science', *Environment and Planning D: Society and Space* 13, 1995, 5-34.

on the changing nature of the public sphere during the eighteenth century, they explore spaces where science was widely discussed, such as cafés and learned societies.[172] Other scholars such as Harold Dorn stress the historically changing culture(s) of science and the situatednesss of science in cultures. His study *The Geography of Science* (1991), moreover, highlighted environmental and material factors shaping the production of knowledge.[173]

The edited volume *Making Space for Science*, published in 1998, similarly reflected this emerging, spatially-minded research perspective. This volume brought together work by leading scholars of the history of science and knowledge. Among the contributors to this volume were Simon Schaffer and Ben Marsden. Their research had increasingly turned to topics ranging from scientific travellers and field observations, to the institutionalisation of professional chairs in Engineering and Mathematics in the mid nineteenth century. It had also come to take in the question of scientific credibility in classrooms and laboratories, physics laboratories in Victorian country houses, and the spatial organisation of astronomy observatories at Manchester University in the 1950s.[174] These and other contributions echoed some of Livingstone's central claims. These comprised, for example, the idea that scientific styles vary substantially between regions and places; that scientific projects and endeavours depend on politics' commitment to science; and that

---

[172] Dorinda Outram, *The Enlightenment*, Cambridge: Cambridge University Press, 2012, pp. 10-25; id., 'New Spaces in Natural History', in Nicholas Jardine, James A. Secord and Emma C. Spary (eds.), *Cultures of Natural History*, Cambridge: Cambridge University Press, 1996, pp. 249-65; Jan Golinski, *Science as Public Culture: Chemistry and Enlightenment in Britain, 1760-1820*, Cambridge: Cambridge University Press, 1992; Jürgen Habermas, *The Structural Transformation of the Public Sphere: An Inquiry into a Category of Bourgeois Society*, Cambridge: Polity, 1989, German 1962; Thomas Broman, 'The Habermasian Public Sphere and "Science *in* the Enlightenment"', *History of Science* 36, 1998, 123-49.

[173] Harold Dorn, *The Geography of Science*, Baltimore: Johns Hopkins University Press, 1991; see also David N. Livingstone and Charles W.J. Withers (eds.), *Geography and Enlightenment*, Chicago and London: University of Chicago Press, 1999; Charles W.J. Withers, *Placing the Enlightenment: Thinking Geographically about the Age of Reason*, Chicago and London: University of Chicago Press, 2007; Charles W.J. Withers and Robert J Mayhew, 'Geography: Space, Place and Intellectual History in the Eighteenth Century', *Journal for Eighteenth-Century Studies* 34, 2011, 445-52; for an important methodological intervention, see Adi Ophir and Steven Shapin, 'The Place of Knowledge: A Methodological Survey', *Science in Context* 4, 1991, 3-21.

[174] Crosbie Smith and Jon Agar (eds), *Making Space for Science: Territorial Themes in the Shaping of Knowledge*, Basingstoke: Palgrave Macmillan, 1998; see also Adriana Craciun and Simon Schaffer (eds.), *The Material Cultures of Enlightenment Arts and Sciences*, London: Palgrave Macmillan, 2016; Ben Marsden, 'Engineering Science in Glasgow: Economy, Efficiency and Measurement as Prime Movers in the Differentiation of an Academic Discipline', *The British Journal for the History of Science* 25, 1992, 319-46.

scientific and learned societies differ from one another according to cultural and social factors.[175]

A most instructive marker of the state of spatially-oriented research in the history of science appeared in 2016 with the publication of *A Companion to the History of Science*.[176] This volume left little room for doubt that the historical geography of science had made their mark on the field. It was edited by Bernard Lightman, professor of humanities, science, and technology at York University, Toronto. The volume's historiographical overview addresses the social construction of scientific knowledge, practice and materiality, the circulation of knowledge, and questions of scale. Empirical chapters focus on scientific actors on the move, such as travelling scientists, and it also casts (amateur) scientists as 'cultural brokers' and 'go-betweens' of places and cultures. Other chapters zoom in on specific places of knowledge production. These include the early modern court, academies, the household, the observatory, and the university.[177] As the *Companion* amply demonstrates, space has come to serve as an analytical category for the historicization of knowledge production. Moreover, it also provides a key concept for making sense of sites of consumption and

---

[175] On the variety of sites of knowledge see, for instance, Anne Secord, 'Science in the Pub: Artisan Botanists in Early Nineteenth-Century Lancashire', *History of Science* 32, 1994, 269-315; Steven Shapin, 'The House of Experiment in Seventeenth-Century England', *Isis* 79, 1988, 373-404; Jan Surman, *Universities in Imperial Austria 1848-1918: A Social History of a Multilingual Space*, West Lafayette: Purdue University Press, 2018; Simon Naylor, 'The Field, the Museum and the Lecture Hall: The Spaces of Natural History in Victorian Cornwell', *Transactions of the Institute of British Geographers* 27, 2002, 494-513; on nineteenth-century American lecture platforms, see now Diarmid A. Finnegan, *The Voice of Science: British Scientists on the Lecture Circuit in Gilded Age America*, Pittsburgh: University of Pittsburgh Press, 2021.

[176] Bernard Lightman (ed.), *A Companion to the History of Science*, Oxford: Wiley-Blackwell, 2016; see also the important volumes by David N. Livingstone and Charles W. J. Withers (eds.), *Geographies of Nineteenth-Century Science*, Chicago and London: University of Chicago Press, 2011; Martin Mahony and Samuel Randalls (eds.), *Weather, Climate, and the Geographical Imagination: Placing Atmospheric Knowledges*, Pittsburgh: University of Pittsburgh Press, 2020; Robert J. Mayhew and Charles W. J. Withers (eds.), *Geographies of Knowledge: Science, Scale, and Spatiality in the Nineteenth Century*, Baltimore: Johns Hopkins University Press, 2020; Simon Naylor and James R. Ryan (eds.), *New Spaces of Exploration: Geographies of Discovery in the Twentieth Century*, London and New York: I.B. Tauris, 2010; as well as the pathbreaking study by Felix Driver, *Geography Militant: Cultures of Exploration and Empire*, Oxford: Blackwell, 2001; and the more recent monograph by Johanna Skurnik, *Making Geographies: The Circulation of British Geographical Knowledge of Australia, 1829-1863*, Turku: University of Turku, 2017.

[177] Lightman (ed.), *Companion to the History of Science*; see also Lorraine Daston and Elizabeth Lunbeck (eds.), *Histories of Scientific Observation*, Chicago and London: University of Chicago Press, 2011; on the household see Alix Cooper, 'Homes and Households', in Katharine Park and Lorraine Daston (eds.), *The Cambridge History of Science*, vol. 3, Cambridge: Cambridge University Press, 2006, pp. 224-37; Mary Terrall, *Catching Nature in the Act: Réaumur and the Practice of Natural History in the Eighteenth Century*, Chicago and London: University of Chicago Press, 2014.

dissemination of knowledge in museums, zoological gardens, world's fairs and other public spaces.[178]

Important inspiration for these spatial approaches to the history of knowledge came from French scholarship. As mentioned in the introduction to *Doing Spatial History*, the French philosopher and historian of science Michel Foucault was of great significance here. His work on hospitals and psychiatry emphasised the role of specific institutional settings in the production of medical knowledge. In works such as *The Order of Things* (1970, French 1966) and *The Archaeology of Knowledge* (1972, French 1969), Foucault also questioned the assumption of a linear, teleological, and progressive development of knowledge. Instead, he argued that scientific thought and academic disciplines went through epistemic breaks and shifts (for instance, during the seventeenth century).[179]

Another key figure has been Bruno Latour, a philosopher, anthropologist, and sociologist of science. Latour is best-known as one of the early proponents of actor-network-theory (ANT). He has also been a major reference point with respect to questions around the institutions of scientific knowledge production. In 1979, Latour and Steve Woolgar published *Laboratory Life: The Social Construction of Scientific Facts*. The two authors carried out an anthropological investigation of scientists at Roger Guillemin's laboratory at the Salk Institute for Biological Studies. They approached the Salk researchers as a foreign 'tribe', and interviewed them in this spirit. Latour and Woolgar showed how, in many respects, a laboratory culture follows unwritten rules and modes of conduct – as does any other culture in a specific place or setting. In terms of the laboratory,

---

[178] Ian Jared Miller, *The Nature of the Beasts: Empire and Exhibition at the Tokyo Imperial Zoo*, Berkeley: University of California Press, 2013; Kirk A. Denton, *Exhibiting the Past: Historical Memory and the Politics of Museums in Postsocialist China*, Honolulu: University of Hawaii Press, 2014; Kendall H. Brown, 'Fair Japan: Japanese Gardens at American World's Fairs, 1876–1940', *SiteLINES: A Journal of Place* 4/1, 2008, 13–16; Christian Tagsold, *Spaces in Translation: Japanese Gardens and the West*, Philadelphia: University of Philadelphia Press, 2017; Mauricio Tenorio-Trillo, *Mexico at the World's Fairs: Crafting a Modern Nation*, Berkeley: University of California Press, 1996.

[179] From the perspective of historical and cultural geography, see Chris Philo, '"A Great Space of Murmurings": Madness, Romance and Geography', *Progress in Human Geography* 37, 2012, 167-94; id., 'A "New Foucault" with Lively Implications: Or "the Crawfish Advances Sideways"', *Transactions of the Institute of British Geographers* 37, 2012, 496-514; see also id., *A Geographical History of Institutional Provision for the Insane from Medieval Times to the 1860s in England and Wales: The Space Reserved for Insanity*, Lampeter: Edwin Mellen, 2004. Foucault's concept 'heterotopia' is taken up by Matt Ylitalo and Sarah Easterby-Smith in Bavaj, Lawson and Struck (eds.), *Doing Spatial History*.

these unwritten rules centred on data collection, the manufacturing of 'raw material', and the production of research papers.[180]

Latour's *Science in Action* (1987) and *The Pasteurization of France* (1988) made a profound impact on the otherwise largely Anglophone field of the history of science. As Latour shows, Louis Pasteur's scientific discovery of microbes has multiple spatial implications. First, microbes are analysed as (non-human) actors in their own right. They need their own experimental spatial arrangements. Observations of microbes take place in specifically arranged and constructed laboratory settings. These serve as 'rooms', in which knowledge is produced and a microbe defined. Furthermore, the laboratory setting serves as a 'theatre of proof' to a scientific audience and wider public.[181]

Latour also laid bare the extent to which, in late nineteenth-century France, the acceptance of a novel scientific fact followed a geographically uneven trajectory. Rejection or acceptance frequently proceeded according to ideological, religious or other factors. Both the production and dissemination of scientific facts were uneven and variegated processes. Site, place, and cultural situatedness played an important role.[182]

When Latour was working on these studies, Steven Shapin and Simon Schaffer published *Leviathan and the Air Pump* (1985). This too has since become a classic. The book focuses on a seventeenth-century debate between Robert Boyle and Thomas Hobbes around the existence and features of the vacuum as a phenomenon. The authors show in great detail that spatial settings and arrangements mattered in the creation of 'truth' and 'scientific fact'. Laboratory science was more than just a source of 'objective knowledge'. It was also a place of spectacle, where experiments were witnessed by trustworthy 'gentlemen scientists' and members of learned societies such as the Royal Society in London.[183]

---

[180] Bruno Latour and Steve Woolgar, *Laboratory Life: The Social Construction of Scientific Facts*, London: Sage, 1979.

[181] Bruno Latour, *The Pasteurization of France*, Cambridge, Mass.: Harvard University Press, 1988, p. 81; see also Simon Schaffer, 'The Eighteenth Brumaire of Bruno Latour', *Studies in History and Philosophy of Science* 22/1, 1991, 175-92.

[182] Bruno Latour, *Science in Action: How to Follow Scientists and Engineers through Society*, Cambridge, Mass.: Harvard University Press, 1987; on the influence of Latour on the geography of science see also Diarmid A. Finnegan, 'Geography of Science', in *International Encyclopedia of the Social & Behavioral Sciences*, 2nd ed., vol. 21, London: Elsevier, 2015, pp. 236-40.

[183] Steven Shapin and Simon Schaffer, *Leviathan and the Air-Pump: Hobbes, Boyle, and the Experimental Life*, Princeton: Princeton University Press, 1985; see also Paula Findlen, 'History of Science: How Buildings Matter', *Journal of the Society of Architectural Historians* 65/1, 2006, 7-8.

The analysis of the spatial settings of laboratories helped develop and differentiate previous explanations of the evolution of science. For example, Thomas Kuhn's *The Structure of Scientific Revolutions* (1962) followed the transition of periods of 'normal science' alongside accepted norms and parameters to relatively sudden ruptures over time. While Kuhn's theory was more time- than space-oriented, his account identified distinct communities of science that operated according to their own internal codes of practice. These and other insights have been further elaborated by sociologist Thomas Gieryn. His concept of 'truth-spots' encapsulates the idea that science is not everywhere the same but differently defined and practiced both across time and space.[184]

If we seek to understand the new avenues that have helped answer spatial questions in the geography of science, then the move by sociologists of knowledge and institutions towards anthropology cannot be underestimated. Fieldwork has provided myriad cultural explanations for the study of 'endangered knowledges' and 'cultures of knowledge'.[185] The notion of the 'field' (Pierre Bourdieu) as a messy, uncontrollable site, and a relatively autonomous social space, has thus become an important analytical and heuristic tool for historians of science.[186] Scholars have drawn on this concept in order to understand the specificity of local knowledge, or cultures of knowledge. We might think here of the work of Fredrik Barth, a Norwegian anthropologist, who explored knowledge in diverse societies and social settings from Indonesia to New Guinea in the 1970s and 1980s. Also relevant is Clifford Geertz' notion of 'local knowledge', which was later appropriated into spatially-informed histories of science.[187]

An account of the multi-faceted reorientation of the history of knowledge towards spatial questions would be incomplete without transnational and global history. From the early 2000s, both approaches have blossomed, as have related

---

[184] Thomas S. Kuhn, *The Structure of Scientific Revolutions*, Chicago and London: Chicago University Press, 1962; Thomas F. Gieryn, *Truth Spots: How Places Make People Believe*, Chicago and London: University of Chicago Press, 2018; see also id., *Cultural Boundaries of Science: Credibility on the Line*, Chicago and London: University of Chicago Press, 1999.

[185] See also Peter Burke, *What is the History of Knowledge?*, Cambridge: Polity, 2016, p. 32.

[186] For an introduction to the notion of 'field' in the history of science, see Henrika Kuklick and Robert E. Kohler, 'Introduction', *Osiris* 11, 1996, 1–14; for empirical studies see André Holenstein, Hubert Steinke and Martin Stuber (eds.), *Scholars in Action: The Practice of Knowledge and the Figure of the Savant in the Eighteenth Century*, 2 vols., Leiden: Brill, 2013.

[187] Among the most influential works are Fredrik Barth, *Ritual and Knowledge among the Baktaman of New Guinea*, Oslo: Universitetsforlaget, 1975; Clifford Geertz, *Local Knowledge: Further Essays in Interpretative Anthropology*, New York: Basic Books, 1983.

concepts ranging from 'entangled history' to 'new imperial history'. These have profoundly impacted the study of the history of science. From the start, transnational and global history emphasised the study of connections across territorial borders. The underlying notion and argument here is that polities, nations, empires, and cultures are not sealed-off containers. In fact, they are porous and, at least, partially shaped by the movement of people, and with them ideas, goods, and commodities.

Until the 1980s, historians tended to foreground the nation as the spatial framework for Enlightenment studies and the 'Scientific Revolution', to name just two examples. However, transnational perspectives question the nation as the primary scale of investigation (though they do not necessarily deny its importance).[188] With its emphasis on movement and connectivity (rather than spatial stasis), there is an inbuilt – yet often implicit – spatial momentum and dynamic in global and transnational history. Only more recently have scholars like Antje Dietze, Katja Naumann, and Ángel Alcalde made the link between space and transnational actors more explicit. They have called for an intensified focus on the arenas in which transnational actors operate, such as congresses or 'epistemic communities'.[189]

Perspectives from both transnational and spatial history have merged to provide a most impactful springboard for historians of science. After all, explorers, travellers, and scientists all travel, as do ideas, instruments, and texts – if not entire laboratories. A key analytical perspective borrowed from transnational history is the concept of 'circulation' as proposed by Pierre-Yves Saunier.[190] Circulation invites the historian to track the translocation of people,

---

[188] Roy Porter and Mikuláš Teich (eds.), *The Enlightenment in National Context*, Cambridge: Cambridge University Press, 1981; id. (eds.), *The Scientific Revolution in National Context*, Cambridge: Cambridge University Press, 1992; for a critical reflection, see Carla Hesse, 'Towards a New Topography of Enlightenment', *European Review of History* 13, 2006, 499-508; Prasenjit Duara, 'Transnationalism and the Challenge to National Histories', in Thomas Bender (ed.), *Rethinking American History in a Global Age*, Berkeley: University of California Press, 2002, pp. 25-46.

[189] Ángel Alcalde, 'Spatializing Transnational History: European Spaces and Territories', *European Review of History* 25, 2018, 553–67; Antje Dietze and Katja Naumann, 'Revisiting Transnational Actors from a Spatial Perspective', in ibid., 415–30; on the concept of 'epistemic communities' see Peter M. Haas, 'Introduction: Epistemic Communities and International Policy Coordination', *International Organization* 46/1, 1992, 1–35; Karin Knorr Cetina, *Epistemic Cultures: How the Sciences Make Knowledge*, Cambridge, Mass.: Harvard University Press, 1999; for the connection between spatial and global history see also the section above on 'Territoriality, Infrastructure and Borders'.

[190] Pierre-Yves Saunier, 'Circulations, connexions et espaces transnationaux', *Genèses* 57, 2004, 110–26; id., *Transnational History*, Basingstoke: Palgrave Macmillan, 2013, pp. 33-78; James A. Secord, 'Knowledge in Transit', *Isis* 95, 2004, 654-72; see also Heike Jöns, 'Transnational Mobility

ideas, and (scientific) objects across space, place, and borders (state, linguistic, cultural), and to analyse their meaning in the new host society. Moreover, it is a call to trace local interactions in the 'field' between different actors involved in the (co-)production of medical, botanical, or cartographic knowledge.

Saunier comes from an urban history background. He does not regard the city as a closed space, but as open to external influences. He also views the city as an entity with the potential to radiate outwards.[191] When Saunier discusses human and non-human connections, his theoretical borrowings from Bruno Latour are abundantly apparent. Indeed, in *The Pasteurization of France*, a key aspect of analysis was the very idea of the translocation and spatially contingent reappropriation of scientific knowledge. And yet, transnational history and the study of 'circulations' have taken this idea a step further. This has occurred both at the level of scales and beyond territorial borders.[192]

More traditional models tended to posit a diffusion of knowledge or ideas from a centre outward to a periphery. But in the wake of the intellectual developments sketched out above, these models have lost analytical traction.[193] For instance, the nexus between colonialism and scientific knowledge (as power and a tool to run empires) has long been established.[194] Historians of science, however, have asked more explicitly about the *where* and the *how* of knowledge production. Martha Few, for instance, has analysed the nature of medical knowledge about a smallpox epidemic in Guatemala, then a Spanish colony, around 1800. She shows how this knowledge was produced as needed on the ground. European notions of science and vaccination certainly played a role here. However, under locally specific circumstances and in the 'field',

---

and the Spaces of Knowledge Production: A Comparison of Different Academic Fields', *Social Geography Discussions* 3, 2007, 79-119.

[191] For examples foregrounding the city as a space of science, knowledge, and technology, see Oliver Hochadel and Agustí Nieto-Galan (eds.), *Barcelona: An Urban History of Science and Modernity, 1888-1929*, London: Routledge, 2016; Stéphane Van Damme, *Paris, capitale philosophique: De la Fronde à la Révolution*, Paris: Odile Jacob, 2005.

[192] See, for instance, Diarmid A. Finnegan and Jonathan Jeffrey Wright (eds.), *Spaces of Global Knowledge: Exhibition, Encounter and Exchange in an Age of Empire*, Farnham: Ashgate, 2015; Diarmid A. Finnegan, 'Scale, Territory, and Complexity: Historical Geographies of Science and Religion', in Bernard Lightman (ed.), *Rethinking History, Science, and Religion: An Exploration of Conflict and the Complexity Principle*, Pittsburgh: University of Pittsburgh Press, 2019, 206-20.

[193] See, for instance, George Basalla, 'The Spread of Western Science', *Science* 156, 1967, 611-22; for a critical review of centre-periphery, see Tessa Hauswedell, Axel Körner and Ulrich Tiedau (eds.), *Re-Mapping Centre and Periphery: Asymmetrical Encounters in European and Global Contexts*, London: UCL Press, 2019.

[194] See, for example, James E. McClellan III and François Regourd, *The Colonial Machine: French Science and Overseas Expansion in the Old Regime*, Turnhout: Brepols, 2011.

Spanish doctors experimented with different vaccines and medications. They did so both in collaboration with and learning from Indigenous medics, and in the face of local resistance. [195] As Londa Schiebinger has shown, local knowledge about the abortive potential of the peacock flower among Amerindians and enslaved women was largely ignored (or unseen) by European explorers and botanists. Transferred from its Caribbean origin, the plant held a primarily aesthetic value and quality in the context of European households and plant collectors.[196]

The vast spatial distance between botanists on both sides of the Atlantic or in far-away colonial outposts in the Caribbean posed both challenges and opportunities. As Sarah Easterby-Smith has demonstrated in *Cultivating Commerce* (2017), long distances gave leeway and thus agency to natural historians on the ground, whether in a colonial botanical garden or among female amateur scientists in England. At the same time, slow communication and the absence of face-to-face communication produced tension, if not mistrust. Distance, space, and a sense of locality thus place in question interpretations that regarded the production of colonial knowledge as a tightly controlled exercise from metropolitan centres.[197]

Such empirical examples pay close attention to the making of knowledge in often far-away locations and under culturally diverse circumstances. They

---

[195] Martha Few, 'Circulating Smallpox Knowledge: Guatemalan Doctors, Maya Indians and Designing Spain's Smallpox Vaccination Expedition, 1780–1803', *The British Journal for the History of Science* 43, 2010, 519–37; id., *For all of Humanity: Mesoamerican and Colonial Medicine in Enlightenment Guatemala*, Tucson: University of Arizona Press, 2015; on hybridity of knowledge in local and regional settings of empire, see Markku Hokkanen and Kalle Kananoja (eds.), *Healers and Empires in Global History: Healing as Hybrid and Contested Knowledge*, Cham: Palgrave Macmillan, 2019.

[196] Londa Schiebinger, 'West Indian Abortifacients and the Making of Ignorance', in Robert N. Proctor and Londa Schiebinger (eds.), *Agnotology: The Making and Unmaking of Ignorance*, Stanford: Stanford University Press, 2008, pp. 149-62; Londa Schiebinger and Claudia Swan (eds.), *Colonial Botany: Science, Commerce, and Politics in the Early Modern World*, Philadelphia: University of Pennsylvania Press, 2005. Eighteenth-century science around botany and natural knowledge paid particularly close attention to specific places and the reappropriation of knowledge. See, for example, Paula Findlen (ed.), *Empires of Knowledge: Scientific Networks in the Early Modern World*, London and New York: Routledge, 2019; Hanna Hodacs, Kenneth Nyberg and Stéphane Van Damme (eds.), *Linnaeus, Natural History and the Circulation of Knowledge*, Oxford: Voltaire Foundation, 2018; Johan Östling et al. (eds.), *Circulation of Knowledge: Explorations into History of Knowledge,* Lund: Nordic Academic Press, 2018. For a critical engagement with the concept of circulation, see Stefanie Gänger, 'Circulation: Reflections on Circularity, Entity, and Liquidity in the Language of Global History', *Journal of Global History* 12, 2017, 303-18.

[197] Sarah Easterby-Smith, *Cultivating Commerce: Cultures of Botany in Britain and France, 1760-1815*, Cambridge: Cambridge University Press, 2017; id., 'Reputation in a Box: Objects, Communication and Trust in Late Eighteenth-Century Botanical Networks', *History of Science* 52, 2015, 180-208.

represent a challenge to common ideas about what constituted European knowledge and the Enlightenment. Such forms of knowledge can, it seems, ultimately be better understood as hybridised products of both European and local, Indigenous knowledge. Indeed, locality and space, as well as the circulation of people, ideas, and objects, matter, in particular, for scholars working on the history of knowledge production in a postcolonial perspective. In *Relocating Modern Science* (2007), Kapil Raj draws on both Latour's work on networks and on Saunier's formulations around the circulation of people and practices in map making. Raj argues that, during the early modern period, 'Western' cartographic techniques were constantly reassembled, adapted, and reformulated in the process of cartographic practices in India. Imperial cartographic knowledge emerged from a constant negotiation between 'power resistance, negotiation, and reconfiguration.'[198]

In 2008, Robert Kohler observed that the wave of 'Lab History' à la Latour may be fading away.[199] But this judgement may have been premature. Katharina Kreuder-Sonnen has explored Polish bacteriologists such as Odo Bujwid, who studied with Robert Koch in Berlin and later Louis Pasteur in 1880s Paris. Kreuder-Sonnen investigates, in particular, how microbes, instruments, and sketches of laboratories travelled to Warsaw. In the early twentieth century, other places such as Kraków and Lemberg became key centres of Polish science and medicine.[200] These and other scientific centres, from Athens to Barcelona and Dublin to Buenos Aires, were not marginal, imitative places of science, in the shadow of Paris or London. In fact, and as Oliver Hochadel and Agustí Nieto-Galan have shown, they were highly dynamic and innovative hubs of scientific knowledge in their own right.[201] In regions like East Central Europe, scientific practices and places of learning, including universities and academies

---

[198] Kapil Raj, *Relocating Modern Science: Circulation and the Construction of Knowledge in South Asia and Europe, 1650-1900*, Basingstoke: Palgrave Macmillan, 2007, p. 343; id., 'Networks of Knowledge, or Spaces of Circulation? The Birth of British Cartography in Colonial South Asia in the Late Eighteenth Century', *Global Intellectual History* 2/1, 2017, 49-66; see also John McAleer, '"A Young Slip of Botany": Botanical Networks, the South Atlantic and Britain's Maritime Worlds, c. 1790-1810', *Journal of Global History* 11, 2016, 24-43.

[199] Robert E. Kohler, 'Lab History: Reflections', *Isis* 99, 2008, 761-8.

[200] Katharina Kreuder-Sonnen, *Wie man Mikroben auf Reisen schickt: Zirkulierendes bakteriologisches Wissen und die polnische Medizin 1885-1939*, Tübingen: Mohr Siebeck, 2018; id., 'From Transnationalism to Olympic Internationalism: Polish Medical Experts and International Scientific Exchange, 1885–1939', *Contemporary European History* 25, 2016, 207–31.

[201] Oliver Hochadel and Agustí Nieto-Galan (eds.), *Urban Histories of Science: Making Knowledge in the City, 1820-1940*, London: Routledge, 2019.

of science, became expressions and symbols of the respective nation, however embedded they were in transnational practices.[202]

## Putting Science in Its Place

David Livingstone's *Putting Science in Its Place* (2003) is a work of synthesis and offers an effective entry point to much of the scholarship discussed and hinted at above. It first explores some of the sites of scientific endeavour, not least the laboratory. Livingstone traces these from the basements of individual homes to the domain of the modern university. A recurring theme here is the interplay between private and public spaces, with scientists relying on the latter as a source of external validity for their otherwise rather solitary endeavours. In a bid to impress 'the experimental public', the laboratory has even served as a theatrical space. Scientists have used laboratories to perform public 'spectacles' – though they sometimes considered such spectacles beneath their dignity. Even more so than laboratories, museums were strongly exposed to the public eye. Livingstone's book shows that curators' 'mental geographies', i.e. the theories they adopted or co-produced, and the way they selected and arranged artefacts and specimens, did not always sit easily with audience expectations. At times, the museum became a veritable 'arena of struggle'.[203]

Livingstone also turns his attention to hospitals and asylums, and their Janus-faced curative and disciplinary functions as 'spaces of diagnosis'. He illuminates the ways in which the very architecture of these regulatory spaces was designed to shape the intended, discipline-centred, morally charged social interaction unfolding within them. They served as 'a sermon in bricks and mortar on the medical benefits of moral discipline'.[204] As well as these brick-and-mortar spaces, Livingstone explores other, more mobile spaces of knowledge production, such as the ship and the tent. He also casts light on the surprising uses of the pub as a site of working-class amateur botany.

A particularly instructive section of *Putting Science in Its Place* considers the regionally constituted nature of scientific knowledge. Livingston does not adopt the deceptive rhetoric of a 'European Scientific Revolution', which has tended to neglect the wealth of inspiration coming from outside of Europe.

---

[202] See Mitchell G. Ash and Jan Surman (eds), *The Nationalization of Scientific Knowledge in the Habsburg Empire, 1848-1918*, Basingstoke: Palgrave Macmillan, 2012.

[203] David N. Livingstone, *Putting Science in Its Place: Geographies of Scientific Knowledge*, Chicago and London: University of Chicago Press, 2003, pp. 23-4, 33-4.

[204] Ibid., pp. 62, 66.

Instead, he makes a case for locating science along 'spatio-temporal coordinates', from 'Edinburgh science' in Enlightenment Scotland to 'Charleston science' in antebellum America. In the case of the 'Manchester model' (Arnold Thackray), a new commercial elite directed its energies towards issues deemed relevant to the industrialised Victorian city. Air pollution and housing quality were of special significance here. In this way, new knowledge was generated and subsequently deployed for purposes of social reform. Furthermore, the reception of scientific theories was often dependent on regional factors. To illustrate these distinct 'geographies of reading', Livingstone tells 'a tale of three cities', a comparative account of how Darwinian evolution was sympathetically received by religious leaders in Presbyterian Edinburgh, just as it was spurned in both Princeton and Belfast, with their politically and religiously contrasting atmospheres.[205]

The circulation of knowledge is a further important focus of Livingstone's book. It investigates, for instance, the ways in which knowledge was transferred home from distant places. It also considers the challenges posed in terms of the validity of knowledge and the trustworthiness of sources. As he observes, 'distance and doubt have always been close companions'. In order to alleviate the dependency on far-off witnesses, scientists resorted to drawings, as well as mapping and photographic techniques, in an attempt to 'obliterate, as far as possible, the space between near and far, here and there, presence and absence'.[206]

At the outset of his book, Livingstone muses on whether 'the craft competencies of the geographer, with an interest in space and place, [could] throw some light on the history of scientific enterprise'. From the point of view of this volume, it would surely be beneficial if some of those 'craft competencies' were to rub off on historians. After all, scientific understanding, as a subject of historical enquiry, is indeed 'always a view from somewhere'.[207]

---

[205] Ibid., pp. 89-90, 115-6.

[206] Ibid., pp. 171, 178.

[207] Ibid., pp. xii, 81, 184.

# 6 Spatial Imaginaries

Spatial imaginaries – such as 'the West', 'Eurasia', and 'the Global South' – take the form of textual, visual or performative representations. They matter because they reduce complexity and shape identities. They do so by homogenising space. They evoke an 'imagined community' (Benedict Anderson), and form part of processes of inclusion and exclusion – determining who is part of this community, and who is not. Spatial imaginaries evoke a sense of belonging and gain traction in response to political challenges: crises, conflicts, and wars. In public discourse, however, geography is typically presented as factual and apolitical, a timeless backdrop to the unfolding of history. All too often spatial imaginaries are taken for granted, their assumptions and intentions left unquestioned.[208] Against this background, scholars have aimed to explore the shifting meanings, political uses, and transnational circulations of spatial imaginaries, through various scales, and across time and space.[209]

An early source of inspiration in this area stems from the term 'cognitive map'. This concept was first introduced in the late 1940s by the American cognitive psychologist Edward C. Tolman. 'Cognitive maps' comprise individual or collective representations of spatial understandings of our environment. As such, they help humans to orient and situate themselves within the world. From the 1960s, the term began to enter other disciplines, including geography and urban planning. Today, scholars make use of a number of approaches and terms. These include 'mental maps', 'spatial semantics', or 'imaginative geographies'.[210]

---

[208] See, for instance, the popular book by Tim Marshall, *Prisoners of Geography*, New York: Scribner, 2015.

[209] For a useful overview see Josh Watkins, 'Spatial Imaginaries Research in Geography: Synergies, Tensions, and New Directions', *Geography Compass* 9/9, 2015, 508-22. Derek Gregory, *Geographical Imaginations*, Oxford: Blackwell, 1994, is often cited in this context, but it deals less with 'spatial imaginaries' than with theoretical imaginations of geographers and methodological approaches to geography.

[210] On 'cognitive' and 'mental maps', see Frithjof Benjamin Schenk, 'Mental Maps: The Cognitive Mapping of the Continent as an Object of Research of European History', *European History Online*, 2013. Available HTTP: <http://www.ieg-ego.eu/schenkf-2013-en> (accessed 10 March 2021); for a definition of 'mental maps' from a psychological perspective, see Roger M. Downs and David Stea, *Maps in Minds*, New York: Harper & Row, 1977, p. 23; Elspeth Graham, 'What Is a Mental Map?', *Area* 8, 1976, 259-62; see also Peter Gould and Rodney White, *Mental Maps*, Harmondsworth: Penguin, 1974; Lawrence A. Hirschfeld and Susan A. Gelman (eds.), *Mapping*

In his book *Orientalism* (1978), literary scholar Edward Said analysed 'imaginative geographies' of the Orient against the historical backdrop of nineteenth century European expansion and colonisation. It focused particularly on textual tropes and spatial rhetoric, such as the 'primitive Arab' or the 'lazy Oriental', as they manifested in travelogues, novels, and geographical writings. Said's sources ranged from the Welsh scholar William Jones to French writers like Gustave Flaubert and learned societies such as the British 'Royal Asiatic Society' (founded in 1823). According to Said, the 'othering' of the Orient created a space of imagination and, crucially, served to facilitate 'Western' imperial and cultural domination. Western representations flattened and homogenised the Orient as 'the other' vis-à-vis the Occident. The Orient became a static, ahistorical, effeminate, passive space, and a region that was lagging behind 'the West'.[211]

Said's postcolonial reading and critique of 'Western' texts about the Orient has sparked controversy and debate. Scholars have critiqued his homogenous treatment not only of the Orient but of the Occident. Indeed, Said mainly analysed British and French voices, thereby homogenising 'the West' or equating it with British and French imperialism.[212] Nonetheless, *Orientalism* continues to be a rich source of inspiration and a reference point for scholars working in the field of spatial imaginaries.[213] From the perspective of spatial

---

the Mind: Domain Specificity in Cognition and Culture, Cambridge: Cambridge University Press, 1994; Juval Portugali (ed.), *The Construction of Cognitive Maps*, Dordrecht: Kluwer, 1996.

[211] Edward W. Said, *Orientalism*, with a new preface, London: Penguin 2003, with a new afterword 1995, first published 1978; see also Derek Gregory, 'Imaginative Geographies', *Progress in Human Geography* 19, 1995, 447-85; id., 'Between the Book and the Lamp: Imaginative Geographies of Egypt, 1849-50', *Transactions of the Institute of British Geographers* 20, 1995, 29-56.

[212] James Clifford, 'Orientalism', *History and Theory* 19, 1980, 204-23; Gyan Prakash, 'Orientalism Now', *History and Theory* 34, 1995, 199-212; Pedro A. Piedras Monroy, 'Edward Said and German Orientalism', *Storia della Storiografia* 44, 2003, 96-103; for a critical engagement with Said see also Robert Irwin, *For Lust of Knowing: The Orientalists and Their Enemies*, London: Penguin, 2007; Urs App, *The Birth of Orientalism*, Philadelphia: University of Pennsylvania Press, 2010.

[213] See, for instance, Thierry Hentsch, *Imagining the Middle East*, New York: Black Rose Books, 1992; Suzanne L. Marchand, *German Orientalism in the Age of Empire: Religion, Race, and Scholarship*, Cambridge: Cambridge University Press, 2009; Timothy Mitchell, *Colonising Egypt*, rev. ed. with new preface, Berkeley: University of California Press, 1991, first published 1988; Elisabeth Oxfeldt, *Nordic Orientalism: Paris and the Cosmopolitan Imagination 1800-1900*, Copenhagen: Museum Tusculanum Press, 2005; Barbara Spackman, *Accidental Orientalists: Modern Italian Travelers in Ottoman Lands*, Liverpool: Liverpool University Press, 2017; Stefan Tanaka, *Japan's Orient: Rendering Pasts into History*, Berkeley: University of California Press, 1993; Vera Tolz, *Russia's Own Orient: The Politics of Identity and Oriental Studies in the Late Imperial and Early Soviet Periods*, Oxford: Oxford University Press, 2011; see also Mark Bassin, *Imperial Visions: Nationalist Imagination and*

history, Said's principal legacy is the idea that spatial concepts are not neutral geographical signifiers; that they carry value-laden assumptions which need to be interrogated; and that they have political effects that need be to be examined. In the past, spatial imaginaries often conveyed meanings of temporalized space, or 'timespace': 'beyond Europe' meant '*before* Europe'; 'moving westward' meant 'moving *forward*'.[214] Spatial imaginaries established hierarchies and created dichotomies along core versus periphery, backward versus modern, civilised versus uncivilised.

The field of spatial imaginaries is vast, and it overlaps with other fields. These comprise the history of travel, borders, geopolitics and cartography, urban history, literary and media studies, and intellectual history.[215] More recently, attempts have been made to address the relative absence of women as historical actors from the history of spatial imaginaries.[216] In practice, scholars

---

*Geographical Expansion in the Russian Far East, 1840-1865*, Cambridge: Cambridge University Press, 1999.

[214] Jon May and Nigel Thrift (eds.), *TimeSpace: Geographies of Temporality*, London and New York: Routledge, 2001; Barney Warf and Santa Arias, 'Introduction: The Reinsertion of Space Into the Social Sciences and Humanities', in id. (eds.), *The Spatial Turn: Interdisciplinary Perspectives*, London and New York: Routledge, 2009, pp. 1-10, here p. 3; Riccardo Bavaj, '"The West": A Conceptual Exploration', *European History Online*, 2011. Available HTTP: <http://www.ieg-ego.eu/bavajr-2011-en> (accessed 31 March 2021). On the idea of 'the West' see Cemil Aydin, *The Politics of Anti-Westernism in Asia: Visions of World Order in Pan-Islamic and Pan-Asian Thought*, New York: Columbia University Press, 2007; Riccardo Bavaj and Martina Steber (eds.), *Germany and The West': The History of a Modern Concept*, New York: Berghahn, 2015; id. (eds.), *Zivilisatorische Verortungen: Der 'Westen' an der Jahrhundertwende (1880-1930)*, Berlin and Boston: De Gruyter, 2018; Michael Kimmage, *The Abandonment of the West: The History of an Idea in American Foreign Policy*, New York: Basic Books, 2020; see also Sebastian Conrad and Dominic Sachsenmaier (eds.), *Competing Visions of World Order: Global Moments and Movements, 1880s-1930s*, New York: Palgrave Macmillan, 2007.

[215] See, for instance, the chapters by David Armitage, 'The International Turn in Intellectual History', and John Randolph, 'The Space of Intellect and the Intellect of Space', in Darrin M. McMahon and Samuel Moyn (eds.), *Rethinking Modern European Intellectual History*, Oxford: Oxford University Press, 2014, pp. 212-31, 232-52; Or Rosenboim, 'Threads and Boundaries: Rethinking the Intellectual History of International Relations', in Nicolas Guilhot and Brian C. Schmidt (eds.), *Historiographical Investigations in International Relations*, Basingstoke: Palgrave Macmillan, 2019, pp. 97-125; see also the classic study on shifting perceptions of space in literature, art, architecture, music, philosophy, sociology, and science in turn-of-the-century Europe by Stephen Kern, *The Culture of Time and Space, 1880-1918*, with a new preface, Cambridge, Mass.: Harvard University Press, 2003, first published 1983.

[216] See Patricia Owens and Katharina Rietzler (eds.), *Women's International Thought: A New History*, Cambridge: Cambridge University Press, 2021; see also Rosenboim, *Emergence of Globalism*, pp. 142-67; as well as more generally Cynthia Enloe, *Bananas, Beaches and Bases: Making Feminist Sense of International Politics*, rev. ed., Berkeley: University of California Press, 2014, first published 1990. A particularly interesting yet underexplored example is Jessie Ackermann, *The World Through a Woman's Eyes*, Chicago: [s.n.], 1896. We thank Ruby Ekkel for drawing our attention to this source.

employ an array of textual sources including travelogues, geographical descriptions, newspapers, and novels, as well as visual sources such as maps, landscape paintings, and photographs.[217] Scholars analyse the construction and meaning of spatial imaginaries on different scales. These include macro-regions, borderlands, and nation-states, as well as smaller units such as sites and cities.

At the global scale, Martin W. Lewis and Kären Wigen have critiqued classification systems centring on continental or macro-regional concepts such as 'Orient' and 'Occident', 'East' and 'West', 'Europe' and 'Asia'. They make a case for critically engaging with such 'metageographies', which have often served to conflate, manipulate and flatten complex social, political, economic, and cultural realities. For example, they dismiss the idea of the 'Third World' as an 'unduly monolithic' political-economic category of the Cold War. Until the concept became redundant when the 'Second World', i.e. the sphere of Soviet communism, transformed after 1989, 'it served the ideological needs of both Cold War American partisans and, on the opposite side of the political spectrum, the most vigorous opponents of American neo-imperialism'.[218]

Indeed, it is important to realize that the concept of the 'Third World' also encapsulated a sense of self-assertion on the part of some so-called 'developing countries'. In 1955, the leaders of many such countries gathered in Bandung to explicitly position themselves against the bipolar order of the Cold War. In doing so, they drew on the concept of the 'Third World', which would later morph into the 'Global South'.[219] Other spatial imaginaries such as the concept of 'one world' became popular during the Cold War too, thanks to anti-Vietnam War protests, an emergent 'North-South dialogue', growing

---

[217] See, for instance, Joan M. Schwartz and James R. Ryan (eds.), *Picturing Place: Photography and the Geographical Imagination*, London and New York: I.B. Tauris, 2003; see also the chapter by James Koranyi in Bavaj, Lawson and Struck (eds.), *Doing Spatial History*.

[218] Martin W. Lewis and Kären Wigen, *The Myth of Continents: A Critique of Metageography*, Berkeley: University of California Press, 1997, pp. 3-4, 196.

[219] See Jürgen Dinkel, *The Non-Aligned Movement: Genesis, Organization and Politics (1927-1992)*, Leiden: Brill, 2018, German 2015; Christoph Kalter, *The Discovery of the Third World: Decolonization and the Rise of the New Left in France, c.1950-1976*, Cambridge: Cambridge University Press, 2016, German 2011; id., 'From Global to Local and Back: The "Third World" Concept and the New Radical Left in France', *Journal of Global History* 12, 2017, 115-36; see also Jürgen Dinkel, Steffen Fiebrig and Frank Reichherzer (eds.), *Nord/Süd: Perspektiven auf eine globale Konstellation*, Berlin and Boston: De Gruyter, 2020; Anne Garland Mahler, *From the Tricontinental to the Global South: Race, Radicalism, and Transnational Solidarity*, Durham: Duke University Press, 2018; Ian Taylor, 'The Global South', in Thomas G. Weiss and Rorden Wilkinson (eds.), *International Organization and Global Governance*, London: Routledge, 2014, pp. 279-91.

environmentalism and global interdependence, as well as Apollo photographs of 'spaceship earth'.[220]

From the 1990s, scholars have increasingly engaged with spatial imaginaries of a range of macro-regions. Mark Bassin and Marlene Laruelle, for example, have investigated the renaissance of post-WWI visions of Eurasianism that followed the collapse of the Soviet Union, and which placed Russia at the core of a civilizational container space defined as anti-liberal and anti-'Western'.[221] Jürgen Osterhammel, in his recently translated *Unfabling the East* (1998), has shown how in Europe, between the late eighteenth and early nineteenth century, the idea of Asia became embedded in an 'exclusive'-Eurocentric, racialized discourse. Asia – and particularly China – came to be regarded as a lesser, declining or stagnant civilisation, a space to be exploited and colonised.[222]

The idea of 'Eastern Europe', too, has been claimed to have emerged during the late eighteenth century – this critical transition period that the German historian of concepts Reinhart Koselleck has called *Sattelzeit* ('saddle time').[223] This at least has been argued by Larry Wolff in his much-discussed, and in part disputed, study *Inventing Eastern Europe* (1994). Along with the rising concept of 'civilisation', travellers (real and armchair) as well as cartographers began to refer to 'Eastern Europe' as an inner-European negative imaginary. Its counterpart was a self-imagined progressive, enlightened '*Western* Europe'.[224]

---

[220] See Denis Cosgrove, *Apollo's Eye: A Cartographic Genealogy of the Earth in the Western Imagination*, Baltimore: Johns Hopkins University Press, 2003; Martin Deuerlein, *Das Zeitalter Der Interdependenz: Globales Denken und internationale Politik in den langen 1970er Jahren*, Göttingen: Wallstein, 2020; David Kuchenbuch, *Welt-Bildner: Arno Peters, Richard Buckminster Fuller und die Mediengeschichte des Globalismus, 1940-2000*, Weimar: Böhlau, 2021; see also, in this context, Helge Jordheim and Erling Sandmo (eds.), *Conceptualizing the World: An Exploration Across Disciplines*, New York and Oxford: Berghahn, 2019.

[221] Mark Bassin, Sergey Glebov and Marlene Laruelle (eds.), *Between Europe and Asia*, Pittsburgh: University of Pittsburgh Press, 2015; Mark Bassin and Gonzalo Pozo (eds.), *The Politics of Eurasianism*, London: Lanham, 2017; Marlene Laruelle (ed.), *Eurasianism and the European Far Right*, London: Lanham, 2015; on the 'imaginary geography' of Sovietness see Emma Widdis, *Visions of a New Land: Soviet Film from the Revolution to the Second World War*, New Haven: Yale University Press, 2003.

[222] See Jürgen Osterhammel, *Unfabling the East: The Enlightenment's Encounter with Asia*, Princeton: Princeton University Press, 2018, German 1998.

[223] The *Sattelzeit* comprises the decades around 1800 (1750-1850). See Reinhart Koselleck, *Futures Past: On the Semantics of Historical Time*, New York: Columbia University Press, 2004, German 1979.

[224] Larry Wolff, *Inventing Eastern Europe: The Map of Civilization on the Mind of the Enlightenment*, Stanford: Stanford University Press, 1994; for a different argument and chronology, which places the origins of the term 'Eastern Europe' in the early and mid-nineteenth century, see the earlier study by Hans Lemberg, 'Zur Entstehung des Osteuropabegriffs im 19. Jahrhundert: Vom

Around the same time, new imaginaries of a North-South fault line evolved on the Italian peninsula, as literary scholar Nelson Moe has shown in *The View from Vesuvius*, which poses the question: 'How and when did southern Italy become "the south", a place and people imagined to be different from and inferior to the rest of the country?' Drawing on both textual and visual sources, Moe traces the origins of this imaginary to foreign writers travelling to Italy, who started to frame what they saw both in terms of backwardness and the 'picturesque'. This was then taken up by northern-based proponents of Italian unification (*Risorgimento*), often poets-cum-politicians, but later also critiqued by a poet like Verga in 'antipicturesque' descriptions of his native Sicily, where 'the South' served as a 'powerful emblem of the failings of national unification'.[225]

The 'use of concepts of place to naturalize uneven structures of rule' is the subject of Kate McDonald's recent study *Placing Empire: Travel and the Social Imagination in Imperial Japan* (2017). What she terms 'spatial politics of empire' concerns early-twentieth-century practices of Japanese colonisation, from Taiwan to the Korean peninsula, and the ways in which travel and tourism were deployed to integrate colonial territories in the imagined realm of the empire, while at the same time distinguishing 'outer territories' from an 'inner territory'. This 'geography of cultural pluralism' was mirrored by restricted mobility and racial discrimination of colonial subjects. This became particularly apparent in

---

"Norden" zum "Osten" Europas', *Jahrbücher für Geschichte Osteuropas* 33, 1985, 48-91; see also Ezequiel Adamovsky, 'Euro-Orientalism and the Making of the Concept of Eastern Europe in France, 1810–1880', *Journal of Modern History* 77, 2005, 591–628; id., *Euro-Orientalism: Liberal Ideology and the Image of Russia in France (c. 1740-1880)*, New York: Peter Lang, 2006; Diana Mishkova and Balázs Trencsényi (eds.), *European Regions and Boundaries: A Conceptual History*, New York: Berghahn, 2017; Willibald Steinmetz, Michael Freeden and Javier Fernández Sebastián (eds.), *Conceptual History in the European Space*, New York: Berghahn, 2017, esp. chapters 8 and 9; as well as the more recent studies by Larry Wolff, *The Idea of Galicia: History and Fantasy in Habsburg Political Culture*, Stanford: Stanford University Press, 2012, and id., *Woodrow Wilson and the Reimagining of Eastern Europe*, Stanford: Stanford University Press, 2020; on the inner-European Orientalist discourse, see also Robert Born and Sarah Lemmen (eds.), *Orientalismen in Ostmitteleuropa: Diskurse, Akteure und Disziplinen vom 19. Jahrhundert bis zum Zweiten Weltkrieg*, Bielefeld: transcript, 2014.

225 Nelson Moe, *The View from Vesuvius: Italian Culture and the Southern Question*, Berkeley: University of California Press, 2002, pp. 1, 194, 275; see also the more recent work by Claudio Fogu, *The Fishing Net and the Spider Web: Mediterranean Imaginaries and the Making of Italians*, Cham: Palgrave Macmillan, 2020; Valerie McGuire, *Italy's Sea: Empire and Nation in the Mediterranean, 1895-1945*, Liverpool: Liverpool University Press, 2020; on southern Europe see also Philipp Müller and Clara Maier (eds.), 'Konstrukt Südeuropa', *Mittelweg*, 36/5, 2018; Martin Baumeister and Roberto Sala (eds.), *Southern Europe? Italy, Spain, Portugal, and Greece from the 1950s to the Present Day*, Frankfurt/Main: Campus, 2015; on 'the North' see, more generally, Peter Davidson, *The Idea of North*, new ed., London: Reaktion, 2016, first published 2005.

the wake of the First World War, when the Japanese Empire was 'moving from treating colonial difference as a matter of time and development to treating colonial difference as a matter of race and place'.[226]

Spatial imaginaries have also been investigated for 'in-between regions' where territorial borders have shifted dramatically over time. East Central Europe has proven particularly fertile in this respect.[227] Ryan Gingeras draws on the example of Ottoman Macedonia to argue that, in British discourses of the early twentieth century, it oscillated between a peripheral European and a 'Near Eastern' position, thus falling 'between the cracks'.[228] At smaller scales, particularly at a local and urban level, the concept of 'mental maps' has also been applied to internalised ideas about cityscapes, infrastructure choices, commuting patterns, and tourist routes.[229]

*Imagining the Balkans*

Maria Todorova's *Imagining the Balkans* (1997) is a classic in the field.[230] The book is distinguished by three key features. First, it offers an impressive variety of sources, including travelogues, media and political commentary, from different contexts: French, English, German, Russian, but also closer to and

---

[226] Kate McDonald, *Placing Empire: Travel and the Social Imagination in Imperial Japan*, Oakland: University of California Press, 2017, pp. 3, 7, 86; see also David L. Howell, *Geographies of Identity in Nineteenth-Century Japan*, Berkeley: University of California Press, 2005; on the geographical consciousness in early modern Japan, see Marcia Yonemoto, *Mapping Early Modern Japan: Space, Place, and Culture in the Tokugawa Period, 1603-1868*, Berkeley: University of California Press, 2003; on China see, moreover, Mark Edward Lewis, *The Construction of Space in Early China*, Albany: State University of New York Press, 2006; Ao Wang, *Spatial Imaginaries in Mid-Tang China: Geography, Cartography, and Literature*, Amherst: Cambria Press, 2018; see also the chapter by Konrad Lawson in Bavaj, Lawson and Struck (eds.), *Doing Spatial History*.

[227] On the idea of 'Central Europe' see most recently Otilia Dhand, *The Idea of Central Europe: Geopolitics, Culture and Regional Identity*, London and New York: I.B. Tauris, 2018; Jessie Labov, *Transatlantic Central Europe: Contesting Geography and Redefining Culture beyond the Nation*, Budapest: Central European University Press, 2019.

[228] Ryan Gingeras, 'Between the Cracks: Macedonia and the "Mental Map" of Europe', *Canadian Slavonic Papers* 50/3-4, 2008, 341–58.

[229] See, for instance, Janet Vertesi, 'Mind the Gap: The London Underground Map and Users' Representations of Urban Space', *Social Studies of Science* 38/1, 2008, 7-33; see also Pamela K. Gilbert (ed.), *Imagined Londons*, Albany: State University of New York Press, 2002, chapters 6 and 7; as well as the above section in this historiographical essay 'City and Home'.

[230] Maria Todorova, *Imagining the Balkans*, New York: Oxford University Press, 1997, updated ed. 2009; on Southeastern Europe see also Dietmar Müller, 'Southeastern Europe as a Historical Meso-Region: Constructing Space in Twentieth-Century German Historiography', *European Review of History* 10, 2003, 393-408; K. E. Fleming, 'Orientalism, the Balkans, and Balkan Historiography', *American Historical Review* 105, 2000, 1218-33.

from within the region itself, including Bulgarian, Greek, and Serbo-Croatian. Second, the work traces the long-term evolution of 'Balkanism'. As Todorova shows, the meaning of this term has changed repeatedly since the early modern period. Third, *Imagining the Balkans* demonstrates that imaginary geographies associated with 'Balkanism' were not only externally driven discourses, but that they were, ultimately, internalised within the region itself.

The historical and historiographical moment of the book's publication is highly relevant here, as is the personal and professional trajectory of the author. Maria Todorova was born in Sofia in 1949. She held academic positions in Bulgaria, before pursuing a career in the US. *Imagining the Balkans* was published at a moment of crisis in the aftermath of the Cold War, the end of state-socialism, and the violent breakup of former Yugoslavia. The book's publication in 1997 reflects a moment when ideological dichotomies and mental maps such as 'East' and 'West' transformed into new hierarchies along spatial lines.

It is not difficult to spot the inspiration of Said's *Orientalism* in Todorova's analysis of the historical origins, trajectories, and legacies of 'Balkanism'. However, and in contrast to Said's static notion of the 'Orient', 'Balkanism' is a constantly shifting geographical category. While writing her book in the 1990s, the discourse on 'Balkanism' as a cipher for chaos, instability, ethnic nationalism, and violence gained new traction due to the breakup of former Yugoslavia. That said, the roots of 'the Balkans' as Europe's 'other within' can be traced back to the late nineteenth century.

Todorova takes her cue from Koselleck's history of concepts. Her book traces the origins, uses, and meanings of the term 'the Balkans' back to the early modern period. Until the eighteenth century, 'the Balkans' served as a signifier of one particular geographical region of the Ottoman Empire. Initially, the term was hardly ever used in non-Ottoman sources.[231] As a geographical term, 'Balkans' only became more widely known outside the region through intensified travel encounters during the nineteenth century. Yet, as Todorova argues, the meaning of the term remained spatially opaque and fairly 'neutral' as a literal translation of Ottoman and Byzantine denominations for the region.[232]

It was only from the late nineteenth century that 'the Balkans' became more frequently used in intellectual and political circles beyond the Ottoman Empire.

---

[231] Todorova, *Imagining the Balkans*, pp. 22-5.
[232] Ibid., p. 26.

This was a historical moment defined by Serbian, Bulgarian, and Romanian independence, and by the 1878 Congress of Berlin. As a geographical concept, 'Balkan Peninsula' or simply 'Balkans' soon replaced a myriad of other geographical concepts. These included 'European Turkey', 'European Ottoman Empire', and 'European Levant'.[233]

In 1903, King Alexander of Serbia and his wife were murdered in Belgrade. Journalistic commentators subsequently intensified a discourse of 'the Balkans' as the inner-European 'other'. This process was exacerbated by the two Balkan Wars of 1912-13 and the assassination of Archduke Ferdinand in 1914, which tipped the region (and soon thereafter the rest of Europe) into war and violence. Western European thinkers, intellectuals, and politicians cultivated the idea of a civilising and imperialist mission based on law, order, cleanliness and other self-attributes. 'The Balkans' became the polar opposite. It was increasingly conceptualised as a region associated with 'cruelty, boorishness, instability, and unpredictability', as well as with disorderly territorial fragmentation.[234]

Despite some criticism it received for errors and omissions, what sets Todorova's work apart is her close attention to events and developments within the region itself. In contrast to the spatially amorphous 'Orient', 'the Balkans' emerge as a concrete place.[235]

---

[233] Ibid., p. 27.

[234] Ibid., pp. 28, 34-35, 119.

[235] See now Diana Mishkova, *Beyond Balkanism: The Scholarly Politics of Region Making*, London and New York: Routledge, 2018; id., 'Spatial Asymmetries: Regionalist Intellectual Projects in East Central Europe in the Interwar Period', in Marja Jalava, Stefan Nygård und Johan Strang (eds.), *Decentering European Intellectual Space*, Leiden: Brill, 2018, pp. 143-64; Timothy Snyder and Katherine Younger (eds.), *The Balkans as Europe, 1821-1914*, Rochester: University of Rochester Press, 2018; see also Vedran Duančić, *Geography and Nationalist Visions of Interwar Yugoslavia*, Cham: Palgrave Macmillan, 2020.

# 7 Cartographic Representations

Spatial imaginaries, of course, can also take the form of cartographic representations. The historical analysis of maps from the viewpoint of visual rhetoric and the production of space gathered momentum since the late 1980s, in conjunction with 'the spatial turn'.

There were, however, important antecedents in cognate disciplines. In 1974, David Woodward, a British-born American cartographer, published an article on the state of the art in his discipline. Woodward worked for many years as curator of maps and cartographic expert at the Newberry Library in Chicago, before returning in 1980 to the University of Wisconsin-Madison, where he had conducted his doctoral research. Woodward lamented what he perceived as a lack of theoretical foundation to the history of cartography. With its principal focus on the technical aspects of map making, cartography seemed to have lost its intellectual raison d'être.[236]

A key intervention was made by Woodward's close colleague Brian Harley. In the 1980s, Harley made a case for dissecting the 'hidden agendas of cartography' as tools of socio-spatial power.[237] After more than 25 years in British academia, Harley relocated to the University of Wisconsin-Milwaukee in 1986. Together with Woodward, he launched the epic *History of Cartography* project. This became instrumental in establishing the field of *critical* cartography.[238] Harley largely dispensed with questions around accuracy and

---

[236] David Woodward, 'The Study of the History of Cartography: A Suggested Framework', *American Cartographer* 1, 1974, 101-15. This was not to suggest that the technical aspects of map making were somehow trivial. Mapping collected data by surveying a three-dimensional space onto a two-dimensional surface is a complex undertaking. It is usually a multi-step, multi-layered, multi-site process. It comprises the surveying of terrain and collecting of data on site through collective fieldwork; a choice of scale and projection; sketching and printing onto a copper plate or lithographic stone. Authorship is often difficult to determine. For a particularly fascinating case of a map of unknown authorship, an early seventeenth-century hand-painted map of East Asia, which has only recently been rediscovered, see Timothy Brook, *Mr. Selden's Map of China: Decoding the Secrets of a Vanished Cartographer*, London: Bloomsbury, 2013.

[237] J.B. Harley, 'Deconstructing the Map', *Cartographica* 26/2, 1989, 1-20, here 3; id., 'Silences and Secrecy: The Hidden Agenda of Cartography in Early Modern Europe', *Imago Mundi* 40, 1988, 57-76; on Harley see, especially, Matthew H. Edney, *The Origins and Development of J.B. Harley's Cartographic Theories*, Toronto: University of Toronto Press, 2005; Denis Wood, 'The Map as a Kind of Talk: Brian Harley and the Confabulation of the Inner and Outer Voice', *Visual Communication* 1/2, 2002, 139-61; see also Daniel Clayton, '"Snapshots of a Moving Target": Harley/Foucault/Colonialism', *Cartographica* 50, 2015, 18-23.

[238] J.B. Harley and David Woodward (eds.), *The History of Cartography*, Chicago and London: Chicago University Press, 1987-present. Since 2005, this monumental project has been directed

technological sophistication. Instead, he advanced a cultural theory-informed reading of maps – one which lay bare both their 'external' and 'internal' power. Such an approach naturally focused on the question of who was behind the creation of a given map – a state agency, for example. However, it also posed the question of which discursive and socially-embedded forces were at work in producing a map.

As mentioned in the introduction to *Doing Spatial History*, 'deconstructing' a map means lifting the veil on the cartographical ideal of 'objectivity', 'accuracy' and 'truthfulness', revealing the 'tricks of the cartographic trade' and unpacking the 'set of rules' inherent to them. It entails the delineation of a particular, historically and culturally conditioned 'mode of visual representation'. [239] Harley's suggested approach to maps has obvious parallels with the approach of his fellow historical geographer Denis Cosgrove's to landscapes, and with that of John Berger to art: They are a 'way of seeing'. [240]

In the 1990s, historians began to pick up on these developments. Jeremy Black and others helped to bring maps as a source to the attention of fellow historians. Soon thereafter, authors such as Jeremy Brotton and Simon Garfield made maps accessible and exciting for a wider public. [241] Another important

---

by Matthew H. Edney. The two latest volumes are Matthew H. Edney and Mary Sponberg Pedley (eds.), *Cartography in the European Enlightenment*, Chicago and London: University of Chicago Press, 2020; Mark Monmonier (ed.), *Cartography in the Twentieth Century*, Chicago and London: University of Chicago Press, 2015.

[239] Harley, 'Deconstructing the Map', 5, 7, 12; see also Jeremy W. Crampton, 'Maps as Social Constructions: Power, Communication and Visualization', *Progress in Human Geography* 25, 2001, 235-52. This tendency has been taken further more recently by Matthew H. Edney, who has made a compelling case for debunking the 'ideal of cartography' as a whole. Edney suggests to confine the meaning of the term 'cartography' to 'Western' Enlightenment-style map making, and to no longer use it in a more generic sense. 'Map studies' and 'map history' would be more appropriate terms here. Matthew H. Edney, *Cartography: The Ideal and Its History*, Chicago and London: University of Chicago Press, 2019, p. 8.

[240] John Berger, *Ways of Seeing*, London: BBC and Penguin, 1972; see also the section above on 'Nature, Environment, and Landscape. In this vein, see most recently Veronica della Dora, *The Mantle of the Earth: Genealogies of a Geographical Metaphor*, Chicago and London: University of Chicago Press, 2021.

[241] See Jeremy Black, *Maps and History: Constructing Images of the Past*, New Haven and London: Yale University Press, 1997; id., *Maps and Politics*, Chicago and London: University of Chicago Press, 1997; id., *Visions of the World: A History of Maps*, London: Mitchell Beazley, 2003; Jerry Brotton, *A History of the World in Twelve Maps*, New York: Penguin, 2012; id., *Great Maps: The World's Masterpieces Explored and Explained*, London: Dorling Kindersley, 2014; Simon Garfield, *On the Map: A Mind-Expanding Exploration of the Way the World Looks*, New York: Gotham Books, 2012; see also Peter Barber and Tom Harper (eds.), *Magnificent Maps: Power, Propaganda and Art*, London: The British Library, 2010; for an earlier example see John Noble Wilford, *The Mapmakers*, London: Pimlico, 1981, rev. ed. 2000; a key work in the German context was Ute

impulse for incorporating maps into the historian's source base came from Benedict Anderson. In the 1991 edition of his famous book *Imagined Communities*, first published in 1983, Anderson added the chapter 'Census, Map, Museum'. In this short and programmatic chapter, Anderson argued that maps were pivotal to the process of nation-building. The production of 'historical maps' served the purpose of creating a 'political-biographical narrative' and of demonstrating the supposed 'antiquity of specific, tightly bounded territorial units'. Originating from the imperial practice of cartographically colour-coding colonies (pink-red in the British case, purple-blue for the French), maps of nation-states entailed a '"jigsaw" effect' that rendered territories seemingly detachable, 'instantly recognizable' and 'everywhere visible': a 'logo-map' which 'penetrated deep into the popular imagination'.[242]

Anderson's book became a springboard and key reference point for a number of historians who asked explicitly spatial questions of maps. The history of cartography has since become a field of cross-disciplinary scholarship, with rich engagement from cartographers, geographers and historians.[243] When surveying the research landscape of the past few decades, three broad areas of

---

Schneider, *Die Macht der Karten: Eine Geschichte der Kartographie vom Mittelalter bis heute*, Darmstadt: Primus, 2004, 4th rev. ed. 2018; see also Christof Dipper and Ute Schneider (eds.), *Kartenwelten: Der Raum und seine Repräsentation in der Neuzeit*, Darmstadt: Primus, 2006.

[242] Benedict Anderson, *Imagined Communities: Reflections on the Origin and Spread of Nationalism*, 2nd ed., London: Verso, 1991 first published 1983, pp. 163, 174-5; see also Patrick Carroll, *Science, Culture, and Modern State Formation*, Berkeley: University of California Press, 2006.

[243] See, especially, Alan M. MacEachren, *How Maps Work: Representation, Visualization, and Design*, New York: Guilford Press, 1995; Mark Monmonier, *How to Lie with Maps*, Chicago and London: University of Chicago Press, 1991, rev. 3rd ed. 2018; Norman J.W. Thrower, *Maps and Civilization: Cartography in Culture and Society*, Chicago and London: University of Chicago Press, 1996 (rev. ed. of *Maps and Man: An Examination of Cartography in Relation to Culture and Civilization*, Englewood Cliffs: Prentice-Hall, 1972); Denis Wood, *The Power of Maps*, London: Routledge, 1993; Tom Conley, *The Self-Made Map: Cartographic Writing in Early Modern France*, Minneapolis: University of Minnesota Press, 1996; Christian Jacob, *The Sovereign Map: Theoretical Approaches in Cartography throughout History*, Chicago and London: University of Chicago Press, 2006, French 1992; see also the more recent work by Mark Monmonier, *Rhumb Lines and Map Wars: A Social History of the Mercator Projection*, Chicago and London: University of Chicago Press, 2010; id., *Connections and Content: Reflections on Networks and the History of Cartography*, Redlands: Esri Press, 2019; Denis Wood with John Fels and John Krygier, *Rethinking the Power of Maps*, New York: Guilford Press, 2010; as well as Ayesha Ramachandran, *The Worldmakers: Global Imagining in Early Modern Europe*, Chicago and London: University of Chicago Press, 2015; Rasmus Grønfeldt Winther, *When Maps Become the World*, Chicago and London: University of Chicago Press, 2020; an accessible guide to the history of cartographic conventions offers Mick Ashworth, *Why North Is Up: Map Conventions and Where They Came From*, Oxford: Bodleian Library, University of Oxford, 2019; for a useful handbook see Alexander Kent and Peter Vujakovic (eds.), *The Routledge Handbook of Mapping and Cartography*, New York: Routledge, 2018.

interest can be identified: the mapping of nations, borderlands, and empires. The work of historian and urban scholar Josef Konvitz offers an early example of critical map studies on the national plane. In 1987, Konvitz explored the link between statecraft and cartography in the mapping of France during the 'long eighteenth century'. This cartographic enterprise was carried out primarily by four generations of the Cassini family; the result was the *Carte Générale de la France* (1747-1818), also known as the 'map of Cassini'. It was initially commissioned by Louis XIV and his minister Jean-Baptiste Colbert in the 1660s. Their goal was to obtain a more granular image of their territory, and to make it 'legible' (James C. Scott) as an object of taxation. The map of Cassini promoted the idea of the hexagon as the seemingly natural shape of France, and it produced an image of France as linguistically homogenous. It gave preference to standardised French for place names and silenced the numerous other languages spoken in France at the time, thus marginalizing lived experience on the ground.[244]

The influence of Harley and Konvitz is very much evident in *Topographies of the Nation* (2002) by David Gugerli and Daniel Speich Chassé, two Swiss historians of science and technology. Their book is a reconstruction of the making of the *Topographical Map of Switzerland* in the nineteenth century. This document has since become known as the 'map of Dufour', because it was named after army officer, engineer and cartographer Guillaume Henri Dufour, who founded the Swiss Federal Office of Topography. As the book shows, the survey of the Alpine landscape was certainly a technical feat. Yet the authors emphasise the purpose and uses of the map, which served as an effective means of communicating the idea of a national territory to a wider audience. One striking example of this was the display of 'the Dufour' at a national exhibition in Zürich.[245]

---

[244] Josef W. Konvitz, *Cartography in France, 1660-1848: Science, Engineering, and Statecraft*, Chicago and London: University of Chicago Press, 1987, with a foreword by Emmanuel Le Roy Ladurie; see also Christine Marie Petto, *When France was King of Cartography: The Patronage and Production of Maps in Early Modern France*, Lanham: Lexington Books, 2007; id., *Mapping and Charting in Early Modern England and France: Power, Patronage, and Production*, Lanham: Lexington Books, 2015; see more generally Jordan Branch, *The Cartographic State: Maps, Territory, and the Origins of Sovereignty*, Cambridge: Cambridge University Press, 2014.

[245] David Gugerli and Daniel Speich, *Topografien der Nation: Politik, kartografische Ordnung und Landschaft im 19. Jahrhundert*, Zürich: Chronos, 2002; see also Daniel Speich, 'Mountains Made in Switzerland: Facts and Concerns in Nineteenth-Century Cartography', *Science in Context* 22, 2009, 387-408.

The similarly mountainous province of Shinano in Japan is explored in Kären Wigen's *A Malleable Map* (2010). This book explores Japan's rich 'chorographic archive' (place-writing) in the form of maps, gazetteers, geographical textbooks, statistical yearbooks, and regional newspapers. Wigen traces the transformation – or rather the 'restoration' – of Shinano into today's Nagano prefecture. She is able to dissect the important role of regional identities in nation-formation, while contributing to cultural geographic understandings of the role of maps in knowledge production and cultural workings of scale.[246]

Latin Americanist Raymond Craib has focused on the case of Mexico to show how government-directed map making was instrumental in producing a seemingly natural and coherent territory. Against the backdrop of its colonial origins, as well as border disputes, maps were an effective (though not unchallenged) tool to both 'stage' Mexico as a sovereign state, and to transform it from a 'space' to a 'place' with which citizens could identify. Maps were adorned, for instance, with artistic imagery that provided 'a visual, historical, and spatial anchor to the plotted points of the abstract grid'. This added a layer of 'foundational mythology' to 'the coordinates that covered, and connected, a cartographic Mexico'. Craib explicitly calls his study a 'spatial history of Mexico'. He draws inspiration from a range of scholars, including Harley, Harvey, Lefebvre, and Paul Carter. His book provides an illuminating example of a study situated at the crossroads of spatial theory, the history of cartography, and – with a focus on property regimes – social history.[247]

---

[246] Kären Wigen, *A Malleable Map: Geographies of Restoration in Central Japan, 1600-1912*, Berkeley: University of California Press, 2010; see also id., Sugimoto Fumiko and Cary Karacas (eds.), *Cartographic Japan: A History in Maps*, Chicago and London: University of Chicago Press, 2016; as well as Carolien Stolte, 'Map-Making in World History: An Interview with Kären Wigen', *Itinerario* 39, 2015, 203-14; see also Kären Wigen, 'Discovering the Japanese Alps: Meiji Mountaineering and the Quest for Geographical Enlightenment', *Journal of Japanese Studies* 31/1, 2005, 1-26; on visual representations and political territorializations of mountains, see more generally Veronica della Dora, *Mountain: Nature and Culture*, London: Reaktion, 2016; Bernard Debarbieux and Gilles Rudaz, *The Mountain: A Political History from the Enlightenment to the Present*, Chicago and London: University of Chicago Press, 2015; on early modern chorography more generally, see the concise overview by Andrew McRae, 'Early Modern Chorographies', *Oxford Handbooks Online*, 2015. Available HTTP: <https://www.oxfordhandbooks.com/view/10.1093/oxfordhb/9780199935338.001.0001/oxfordhb-9780199935338-e-102> (accessed 31 March 2021); on chorography and late medieval english maps, see Matthew Boyd Goldie, *Scribes of Space: Place in Middle English Literature and Late Medieval Science*, Ithaca: Cornell University Press, 2019, pp. 18-54.

[247] Raymond B. Craib, *Cartographic Mexico: A History of State Fixations and Fugitive Landscapes*, Durham: Duke University Press, 2004, pp. 7, 34; see also id., 'Cartography and Decolonization', in James R. Akerman (ed.), *Decolonizing the Map: Cartography from Colony to Nation*, Chicago and

Of course, maps were used not only with the intention of consolidating territory but also with the aim of expanding it. As mentioned in the introduction to *Doing Spatial History*, the legacy of cartography in Weimar and Nazi Germany partly explains why many German historians after 1945 shied away from including maps in their work, even for merely illustrative purposes. Two important studies by geographer Guntram Herb and historian David Thomas Murphy, both published in 1997, offer a critical and suitably contextualized engagement with German map making in the first half of the twentieth century. They elucidate the 'use value' of various kinds of maps – from post-Versailles Treaty revisionism to National Socialist expansionism. They draw on several kinds of maps, from the 'scientific' variant, which maintained an aura of objective accuracy, to more 'suggestive' maps. The later were replete with starkly black-and-white visual rhetoric and swooping arrows; they made no bones about their propagandistic goals.[248] Relevant here is Kristin Kopp's more recent analysis of *Germany's Wild East: Constructing Poland as Colonial Space* (2012). This book offers a Harley- and Anderson-inspired model of how to 'read' maps. It casts a close eye on 'sign systems' and colour-coding in order to lay bare the (German) territorial claims and (Polish) ethnographic silences inscribed in maps.[249]

Indeed, East Central Europe has been a particularly contested region,

---

London: University of Chicago Press, 2017, pp. 11-71; equally inspired by Harley and Lefebvre is Ricardo Padron, *The Spacious Word: Cartography, Literature, and Empire in Early Modern Spain*, Chicago and London: University of Chicago Press, 2004; see also id., *The Indies of the Setting Sun: How Early Modern Spain Mapped the Far East as the Transpacific West*, Chicago and London: University of Chicago Press, 2020; Nancy P. Applebaum, *Mapping the Country of Regions: The Chorographic Commission of Nineteenth-Century Colombia*, Chapel Hill: University of North Carolina Press, 2016; Walter D. Mignolo, *The Darker Side of the Renaissance: Literacy, Territoriality, and Colonization*, Ann Arbor: University of Michigan Press, 1995, esp. part 3 ('The Colonization of Space'); Neil Safier, *Measuring the New World: Enlightenment Science and South America*, Chicago and London: University of Chicago Press, 2008; on Indigenous mapping see Barbara E. Mundy, *The Mapping of New Spain: Indigenous Cartography and the Maps of the Relaciones Geográficas*, Chicago and London: University of Chicago Press, 1996; id., 'History in Maps from the Aztec Empire', in Kären Wigen and Caroline Winterer (eds.), *Time in Maps: From the Age of Discovery to Our Digital Era*, Chicago and London: University of Chicago Press, 2020, pp. 79-102; Reuben Rose-Redwood et al., 'Decolonizing the Map: Recentering Indigenous Mappings', *Cartographica* 55/3, 2020, 151-62; as well as Candace Fujikane, *Mapping Abundance for a Planetary Future: Kanaka Maoli and Critical Settler Cartographies in Hawai'i*, Durham: Duke University Press, 2021.

[248] Guntram Henrik Herb, *Under the Map of Germany: Nationalism and Propaganda, 1918-1945*, London: Routledge, 1997; David Thomas Murphy, *The Heroic Earth: Geopolitical Thought in Weimar Germany, 1918-1933*, Ohio: Kent State University Press, 1997; Ulrike Jureit, *Das Ordnen von Räumen: Territorium und Lebensraum im 19. und 20. Jahrhundert*, Hamburg: Hamburger Edition, 2012.

[249] Kristin Kopp, *Germany's Wild East: Constructing Poland as Colonial Space*, Ann Arbor: University of Michigan Press, 2012, esp. chapter 4.

marked by wars, imperial contests, and the constant redrawing of borders. Historian Steven Seegel has taken the long view here, from the late eighteenth century to the Treaty of Versailles. His work on Russian cartography provides an analysis of military, ethnographic and linguistic maps, as well as state-sponsored topographical surveys, geographical writings, and cartographic classroom material. Seegel draws on, but also problematises, Anderson's arguments. He focuses on a region contested by empires, 'small nations', and 'fantasy spaces' such as 'European Russia', 'Habsburg Galicia', or a German-dominated 'Central Europe' (*Mitteleuropa*). In such regions, maps 'were intended not only to describe the empire's multi-ethnic lands and peoples between apparent "natural boundaries", but also to civilize designated regions by applying […] Orientalist hierarchies to legitimize the conquest and retention of land'.[250]

The contours of Anderson's 'logo map' become equally blurred in Alsace-Lorraine, another contested European border region. This case has been examined by Catherine Dunlop in *Cartophilia* (2015). The border between France and Germany, or the German lands, constantly shifted between 1792 and 1918. Against this background, cartographic material became instrumental in disputes over territorial claims. There was no one 'logo map' here. Naturally, the cartographic battle over Alsace and Lorraine was fought by official cartographers in distant Berlin and Paris. Moreover, however, it was also fought regionally and locally, by classroom teachers, geographical societies, and amateur mapmakers. Harley suggested that state-sponsored maps may have '"desocialized" territories […] by reducing the social and cultural complexity of territory to a coldly calculated system of signs and measurements'. Dunlop, however, places much emphasis on maps as a 'positive form of *self-identification*

[250] Steven Seegel, *Mapping Europe's Borderlands: Russian Cartography in the Age of Empire*, Chicago and London: University of Chicago Press, 2012, p. 6; see also his more recent work *Map Men: Transnational Lives and Deaths of Geographers in the Making of East Central Europe*, Chicago and London: University of Chicago Press, 2018; as well as Catherine Gibson, 'Shading, Lines, Colors: Mapping Ethnographic Taxonomies of European Russia', *Nationalities Papers* 46, 2018, 592-611; Jennifer Keating, 'Imperial Maps', in George Gilbert (ed.), *Reading Russian Sources: A Student's Guide to Text and Visual Sources from Russian History*, London and New York, 2020, pp. 61-76; Tomasz Kamusella, Motoki Nomachi and Catherine Gibson (eds.), *Central Europe through the Lens of Language and Politics: On the Sample Maps from the Atlas of Language Politics in Modern Central Europe*, Sapporo: Slavic-Eurasian Research Center, Hokkaido University, 2017; for an analysis of ethnographic maps in the Russian empire and the 'making of Lithuanians', see Vytautas Petronis, *Constructing Lithuania: Ethnic Mapping in Tsarist Russia, ca. 1800-1914*, Stockholm: Intellecta, 2007; see also, in this context, the chapter by Bernhard Struck in Bavaj, Lawson and Struck (eds.), *Doing Spatial History*.

for members of a society'. 'Mapping nations into being' also involved on-the-ground 'counter-mapping', through 'village maps, hiking maps, and urban maps'.[251]

Matthew Edney's landmark study *Mapping an Empire* (1997) was published nearly two decades before Seegel's and Dunlop's work. Edney followed more closely in Harley's footsteps. The influence of Said, Foucault, and Paul Carter is also evident. This book focuses on the process of mapping British India in the late-eighteenth and early-nineteenth centuries. Edney draws on examples such as James Rennell's 'Bengal Atlas' (1779) and 'Map of Hindoostan' (1782) in order to demonstrate in great detail that geographical knowledge production and map making were fundamental to imperial control: 'To govern territories, one must know them.'

Edney shows how the perceived accuracy of the data gathered and the maps produced were transformed by the introduction of triangulation as a mathematical framework for surveying. The trigonometrical basis of triangulation provided what Edney describes as a 'technological fix' for human error in the surveying process. This brought the East India Company ever closer to their 'cartographic ideal'. As Edney writes, 'at one uniform scale, all portions of Indian space became directly comparable and normalized'. This homogenization of knowledge, however imperfect and incomplete in reality, acted as 'a disciplinary mechanism, a technology of vision and control, which was integral to British authority in South Asia'.[252] From the late nineteenth century, this kind of 'command cartography' was subverted by Indian artists and printmakers. As 'barefoot cartographers', these actors produced a variety of anthropomorphic maps and cartographic images of 'Mother India'. This is

---

[251] Catherine Dunlop, *Cartophilia: Maps and the Search for Identity in the French-German Borderland*, Chicago and London: University of Chicago Press, 2015, pp. 7-8, 11-12, 14 (original emphasis); see J.B. Harley, 'Maps, Knowledge, and Power', in Cosgrove and Daniels (eds.), *Iconography of Landscape*, pp. 277-312, here p. 303. The term 'counter-maps' is borrowed from Nancy Lee Peluso, 'Whose Woods Are These? Counter-Mapping Forest Territories in Kalimantan, Indonesia', *Antipode* 27, 1995, 383-406; see also the more recent adaptation in Julie MacArthur, *Cartography and the Political Imagination: Mapping Community in Colonial Kenya*, Athens: Ohio University Press, 2016, esp. pp. 20-2.

[252] Matthew H. Edney, *Mapping an Empire: The Geographical Construction of British India, 1765-1843*, Chicago and London: University of Chicago Press, 1997, pp. 1, 25-6, 39; see also James R. Akerman (ed.), *The Imperial Map: Cartography and the Mastery of Empire*, Chicago and London: University of Chicago Press, 2009; for the adoption of modern mapping techniques in the building of the Qing empire in southwest China, see Laura Hostetler, *Qing Colonial Enterprise: Ethnography and Cartography in Early Modern China*, Chicago and London: University of Chicago Press, 2001.

vividly depicted in Sumathi Ramaswamy's *The Goddess and the Nation* (2010), a fascinating mix of visual history, history of cartography, and gender studies.[253]

Toponymy, the study of place names, takes centre stage in Daniel Foliard's more recent reading of British imperial maps. Foliard is clearly inspired by Lewis and Wigen's *The Myth of Continents*, as well as by the work of other geographers such as Felix Driver, Derek Gregory, and again Brian Harley. He traces the origins of the term 'Middle East' through British maps from the mid nineteenth century. In fact, it was only during the heyday of Britain's multi-directional expansion that the term became commonplace. This process was shaped by maps, which served not only as a form of geographical knowledge, but also as an expression of ignorance. In both regards, maps proved crucial for forging a notion of the 'Middle East' in the context of a rapidly growing market of map readers. As Foliard shows, map making can thus be understood as a performative act.[254]

Already before the publication of Foliard's book, mass-market cartography had served as a prominent subject in Susan Schulten's *The Geographical Imagination in America* (2001). This contribution also examined school geography and the *National Geographic*.[255] Cartography had once been a 'science of princes'.[256] By the late nineteenth century, however, it had entered the realm of mass consumption. Maps became much more widely available, in the form of school and world atlases, as well as war atlases – war, after all, was often a prime mover in transforming, and globalising, geographical imaginations. At the same time, maps also began to appear as 'tools of inquiry', in fields such as science, medicine, education, and governance. This second point is emphasised in

---

[253] Sumathi Ramaswamy, *The Goddess and the Nation: Mapping Mother India*, Durham: Duke University Press, 2010, pp. 33-55, 236; for context, see also Manu Goswami, *Producing India: From Colonial Economy to National Space*, Chicago and London: University of Chicago Press, 2004.

[254] Daniel Foliard, *Dislocating the Orient: British Maps and the Making of the Middle East, 1854-1921*, Chicago and London: University of Chicago Press, 2017, pp. 4-7; for nineteenth-century German and European geographical views on Africa, see Iris Schröder, *Das Wissen von der ganzen Welt: Globale Geographien und räumliche Ordnungen Afrikas und Europas 1790-1870*, Paderborn: Schöningh, 2011.

[255] Susan Schulten, *The Geographical Imagination in America 1880-1950*, Chicago and London: University of Chicago Press, 2001; see also, in this context, Martin Brückner, *The Geographic Revolution in Early America: Maps, Literacy, and National Identity*, Chapel Hill: University of North Carolina Press, 2006; id. (ed.), *Early American Cartographies*, Chapel Hill: University of North Carolina Press, 2011; id., *The Social Life of Maps in America, 1750-1860*, Chapel Hill: University of North Carolina Press, 2017; for an earlier 'publishing boom' in Late Ming China, beginning in the mid-sixteenth century, see Alexander Akin, *East Asian Cartographic Print Culture: The Late Ming Publishing Boom and its Trans-Regional Connections*, Amsterdam: Amsterdam University Press, 2021.

[256] Harley, 'Maps, Knowledge, and Power', p. 281.

Schulten's more recent book *Mapping the Nation* (2012). Designed with the intent to 'identify spatial patterns and relationships', a whole range of new types of maps emerged during the nineteenth century. This included weather maps, climate maps, census maps, medical maps, maps of Indigenous migrations (such as Emma Willard's 1828 map), and maps amounting to a 'cartography of slavery'. 'The world we inhabit today – saturated with maps and graphic information', writes Schulten, 'grew from this sea change in spatial thought and representation'.[257]

Various other examples in the history of cartography have tended to highlight the interrelationship between geographical knowledge, territorial control, and social homogenisation. Schulten's study, however, focuses on maps deliberately created as visual arguments that could show both national coherence and internal fragmentation – socially, medically, ethnically, and environmentally. As can be gleaned from John F. Smith's *Historical Geography* (1888) or Charles O. Paullin and John K. Wright's *Atlas of the Historical Geography of the United States* (1932), they could also map time.[258] Exploring the multitude of 'cartographic representations of temporality' has now evolved into a particularly promising trend in the history of cartography.[259]

Like the nineteenth century, the twentieth century was also a crucial period in the evolution of map making. This is the subject of William Rankin's

---

[257] Susan Schulten, *Mapping the Nation: History and Cartography in Nineteenth-Century America*, Chicago and London: University of Chicago Press, 2012, pp. 2-3, 8, 127-33 ('cartography of slavery'); see also id., *A History of America in 100 Maps*, London: The British Library, 2018; for case studies on female mapmakers see Christina E. Dando, *Women and Cartography in the Progressive Era*, London and New York: Routledge, 2018; Catherine Gibson, 'Mapmaking in the Home and Printing House: Women and Cartography in Late Imperial Russia', *Journal of Historical Geography* 67, 2020, 71-80; for a model study on medical maps, see Pamela K. Gilbert, *Mapping the Victorian Social Body*, Albany: State University of New York Press, 2004; on the relationship between statistics, cartography, and the 'social body', see Wolfgang Göderle, *Zensus und Ethnizität: Zur Herstellung von Wissen über soziale Wirklichkeiten im Habsburgerreich zwischen 1848 und 1910*, Göttingen: Wallstein, 2016; Jason D. Hansen, *Mapping the Germans: Statistical Science, Cartography, and the Visualization of the German Nation, 1848-1914*, Oxford: Oxford University Press, 2015; on cartographic representations of the physical world, see Denis Wood and John Fels, *The Natures of Maps: Cartographic Constructions of the Natural World*, Chicago and London: University of Chicago Press, 2008.

[258] See Schulten, *Mapping the Nation*, pp. 41-76; id., 'How Place Became Process: The Origins of Time Mapping in the United States', in Wigen and Winterer (eds.), *Time in Maps*, pp. 171-92.

[259] The recent volume by Wigen and Winterer (eds.), *Time in Maps*, shows a great variety of approaches to 'decoding temporal messages' in what is typically considered a 'spatial medium'. Id., 'Introduction: Maps Tell Time', in ibid., pp. 1-13, here p. 2; see also Zef Segal and Bram Vannieuwenhuyze (eds.), *Motion in Maps, Maps in Motion: Mapping Stories and Movement Through Time*, Amsterdam: Amsterdam University Press, 2020.

important study *After the Map* (2016). Rankin's book is informed by spatial theory, and it is situated at the intersection of the history of cartography, infrastructure and territoriality. He identifies an 'epistemic shift' which occurred in the middle of the twentieth century. During the First World War, a latitude and longitude-based form of spatial representation was still dominant. By the time of the Cold War, however, a dotted grid-system had been put to widespread use. Rankin argues that this new 'geo-epistemology' was precipitated by technologies like civil aviation as well as nuclear and other long-distance weapon systems. This epistemology was no longer beholden to any truth claims, but put utility first. *After the Map* thus points to coordinate-based visual moves *beyond* cartographic representation.[260]

### Siam Mapped

As mentioned, when Benedict Anderson published an updated edition of his pioneering *Imagined Communities* in 1991, he added a chapter titled 'Census, Map, Museum'. In the preface to the new edition, he confessed to having become 'uneasily aware that what I had believed to be a significantly new contribution to thinking about nationalism – changing apprehensions of time – patently lacked its necessary coordinate: changing apprehensions of space. A brilliant doctoral thesis by Thongchai Winichakul, a young Thai historian, stimulated me to think about mapping's contribution to the nationalist imagination.'[261] The thesis that inspired Anderson to take up the question of space and maps was published a few years later in 1994 as *Siam Mapped: A History of the Geo-Body of a Nation*.[262]

In the reissue of *Imagined Communities*, more than half of the new material dedicated to maps comprises a summary of Thongchai's arguments. In this way, Anderson's classic text on nationalism has introduced countless students to the key theses of *Siam Mapped*. Thongchai argues that, up until the mid-nineteenth century, visual depictions of space in Siam (today's Thailand) were different,

---

[260] William Rankin, *After the Map: Cartography, Navigation and the Transformation of Territory in the Twentieth Century*, Chicago and London: University of Chicago Press, 2016; on Cold War cartography, see also Timothy Barney, *Mapping the Cold War: Cartography and the Framing of America's International Power*, Chapel Hill: University of North Carolina Press, 2015; Matthew Farish, *The Contours of America's Cold War*, Minneapolis, University of Minnesota Press, 2010; id., 'Cold War Planet', in Domosh, Heffernan and Withers (eds.), *Handbook of Historical Geography*, vol. 2, pp. 519-36.

[261] Anderson, *Imagined Communities*, pp. xiii-xiv.

[262] Thongchai Winichakul, *Siam Mapped: A History of the Geo-Body of a Nation*, Honolulu: University of Hawaii Press, 1994.

more diverse, and could simultaneously represent sacred topographies of pilgrimage and power as well as the sovereignty of kingship. *Siam Mapped* also shows how concepts that resembled Western boundaries existed in pre-modern Siam, but that they functioned very differently. All of the Thai terms denoted areas or frontiers – 'thick lines' with a 'broad horizontal extent' – which existed *between* limits of territory. Thongchai also contends that the increasing dominance of a new science of mapping and surveying from the mid-century onwards played a decisive role in the emergence of a new abstract bounded territory. This was, in fact, the recognisable *geo-body* of a modern Siamese nation.[263]

As a spatial history, *Siam Mapped* embraced several of the approaches addressed in this guide. It explored lived practices in Siam's boundary zones; the complex spatial implications of shared sovereignty between the various polities in the region; and the evolving Thai lexicons of space. In terms of its specific contribution to thinking about maps and space, Thongchai's most important contribution comes in the book's fifth to eighth chapters. These comprise a narrative of the rise of the *geo-body* of Siam.

Thongchai lays bare the inner mechanics of a new science of mapping. First, the material production of these maps were spatial claims on territory. These were deployed – like soldiers – in the frontier disputes between Siam and its encroaching French and British imperial neighbours. The *geo-body* of Siam was created out of the 'space left over from direct colonialism' in French Indochina and British Burma. However, as Siam abandoned its Indigenous practices of political space and shared sovereignty, it ceased to be a mere victim of Western colonialism.[264] This brings us to Thongchai's second point: the new science of mapping played a crucial role in a comprehensive 'internal' campaign of modernising 'reforms'. This programme concealed Siam's own campaign of conquest and domination over polities that had once enjoyed broad autonomy and claimed multiple overlords.[265] Once Siam was 'bounded' externally, and its multiple internal sovereignties flattened, the new *geo-body* was complete. It became a powerful symbol, anachronistically projected into the past in the process of creating national narratives of history.[266]

---

[263] Anderson's summary is in *Imagined Communities*, pp. 171-4.

[264] Thongchai, *Siam Mapped*, p. 131.

[265] Ibid., pp. 143-9.

[266] Ibid., pp. 150-6.

# 8 Historical GIS

As mentioned in the introduction to *Doing Spatial History*, a growing literature has come to refer to 'spatial history' as an alternative term for scholarship driven by the tools and approaches of historical geographic information systems (HGIS). Thus, for some, 'spatial history' provides an elegant alternative to a clunky acronym. A GIS refers to a 'system', often a piece of software and its supporting components, which create or interact with one or more geographic databases and allow researchers to analyse, explore, and visualise the information in these databases.[267] Among some practitioners, though less commonly among historians, the maturation of the technology, and the community of scholars who use it, has resulted in a replacement of 'system', in 'GIS', with 'science'. GIS technology has become an important component of research in a wide range of fields. It has expanded beyond its early home of geography to the biological and social sciences. In humanities subjects other than history, for example, scholars of literature have also made productive use of GIS's tools and methodologies as part of a more interdisciplinary 'humanities GIS' or 'spatial humanities'.[268]

The use of GIS technologies for historical research and the development of HGIS as a distinct field took shape in the late 1990s. There were sessions on HGIS at two annual conferences of the Social Science History Association in 1998 and 1999. In 2000, the historical geographer Anne Kelly Knowles edited an important special issue in *Social Science History* entitled 'Historical GIS: The Spatial Turn in Social Science History.'[269] In the first decade of the new millennium, Ian N. Gregory, a geographer and now professor of digital humanities, authored two early methodological introductions.[270] One

---

[267] Ian N. Gregory and Paul S. Ell, *Historical GIS: Technologies, Methodologies and Scholarship*, Cambridge: Cambridge University Press, 2007, pp. 2-5.

[268] Peta Mitchell, 'Literary Geography and The Digital: The Emergence of Neogeography', in Tally (ed.), *Routledge Handbook of Literature and Space*, pp. 85-94, here p. 93; David J. Bodenhamer, John Corrigan and Trevor M. Harris (eds.), *The Spatial Humanities: GIS and the Future of Humanities Scholarship*, Bloomington: Indiana University Press, 2010; see also David Cooper (ed.), *Literary Mapping in the Digital Age*, London and New York: Routledge, 2016, and Barbara Piatti, 'Literary Cartography: Mapping as Method', in Engberg-Pedersen (ed.), *Literature and Cartography*, pp. 45-72.

[269] Anne Kelly Knowles also made use of GIS to explore the development of the US iron industry in her award-winning book, *Mastering Iron: The Struggle to Modernize an American Industry, 1800-1868*, Chicago and London: University of Chicago Press, 2013.

[270] Gregory and Ell, *Historical GIS*; Ian Gregory, *A Place in History: A Guide to Using GIS in Historical*

important volume which reflected on the impact of GIS in history was *Placing History: How Maps, Spatial Data, and GIS are Changing Historical Scholarship* (2008). In this contribution, Anne Kelly Knowles argued that the emerging field of HGIS shares four characteristics: (1) geographical questions 'drive a significant part' of historical research, (2) geographical information provides a 'good share' of its evidence, (3) this evidence is 'structured and analysed within one or more databases that record both location and time,' and (4) the resulting arguments are 'presented in maps' as well as other more traditional mediums.[271]

In 2010, two years after the publication of Knowles' book, another important intervention was made by Richard White, an environmental historian and the director of the 'Spatial History Project' at Stanford University. White described this project as part of a 'larger spatial turn in history'. However, he singled out GIS as particularly well-equipped to explore dynamic processes in motion, juxtapose representations of space for analysis, and go beyond mere illustration in the form of static maps to offer new methodologies for historical research.[272] Indeed, the gallery of projects hosted by the Center for Spatial and Textual Analysis offers an impressively diverse sample of an approach to spatial history. This approach emphasises the power of visualisation, often in highly interactive interfaces. The ultimate goal is to explore 'patterns of movement and transformation in the past.'[273]

What does this scholarship actually look like? Six key edited collections of work on HGIS helped set the direction for work in this field. These are *Past Time, Past Place* (2002), the above mentioned *Placing History* (2008), *The Spatial Humanities* (2010), *History and GIS* (2013), *Toward Spatial Humanities* (2014), and *The Routledge Companion to Spatial History* (2018).[274] Prominent in these works on

---

*Research*, Oxford: Oxbow Books, 2003. For a survey of the early period, see Ian N. Gregory and Richard G. Healey, 'Historical GIS: Structuring, Mapping and Analysing Geographies of the Past', *Progress in Human Geography* 31, 2007, 638-53.

[271] Anne Kelly Knowles and Amy Hillier (eds.), *Placing History: How Maps, Spatial Data, and GIS are Changing Historical Scholarship*, Redlands: Esri Press, 2008, p. 7.

[272] Richard White, 'What is Spatial History?', *The Spatial History Project*, February 2010. Available HTTP:<https://web.stanford.edu/group/spatialhistory/cgi-bin/site/pub.php?id=29> (accessed 31 March 2021).

[273] Spatial History Project gallery. Available HTTP:

<https://web.stanford.edu/group/spatialhistory/cgi-bin/site/gallery.php> (accessed 10 January 2021). The Stanford Literary Lab, founded in 2010, is another project at Stanford using GIS technologies in some of its projects studying literature. Available HTTP: <https://litlab.stanford.edu/> (accessed 31 March 2021).

[274] Knowles and Hillier (eds.), *Placing History*; Ian Gregory and Alistair Geddes (eds.), *Toward Spatial Humanities: Historical GIS and Spatial History*, Bloomington: Indiana University Press, 2014;

HGIS has been an emphasis on the *heuristic* value of GIS as a part of the scholarly process of discovery.[275] Much of the GIS-informed historical work published in the past two decades uses the creation of a GIS as a starting point to identify new questions or areas for further research. It has also explored the interplay between different kinds of data, helped to identify patterns, and generally served to orient the historian as they explore their material. Larger scale historical GIS projects such as the China Historical GIS or the Lyons Historical GIS projects usually incorporate sources and materials that go far beyond what can be justified by the ambitions of any single historical project. They draw sustained interest and funding from their capacity to serve as a starting point for more open-ended explorations of historical space.[276]

Maps are a useful – but not always a necessary – output for exploring spatial databases. One often overlooked tool in this area is the digital gazetteer. It may claim ties to the rich traditions of chorography, or 'place-writing', that may be found in many societies that developed gazetteers.[277] This plays an important role for historians and other scholars in the humanities. It is, essentially, a rich and extensive list of locations and supporting information about them.[278] A

---

Bodenhamer, Corrigan and Harris (eds.), *The Spatial Humanities*; Ian Gregory, Don DeBats and Don Lafreniere (eds.), *The Routledge Companion to Spatial History*, London: Routledge, 2018; Anne Kelly Knowles (ed.), *Past Time, Past Place: GIS for History*, Redlands: Esri Press, 2002. Another recently published collection is Charles Travis, Francis Ludlow and Ferenc Gyuris (eds.), *Historical Geography, GIScience and Textual Analysis: Landscapes of Time and Place*, Cham: Springer, 2020, which also includes chapters employing computational text analysis. One useful list of publications and resources related to HGIS is the Historical GIS Research Network. Available HTTP: <http://www.hgis.org.uk/> (accessed 1 January 2021).

[275] See, for example, this exploratory approach in Nicholas Terpstra and Colin Rose (eds.), *Mapping Space, Sense, and Movement in Florence: Historical GIS and the Early Modern City*, London and New York: Routledge, 2016. In his use of historical GIS, Brian Donahue speaks of 'interpretive maps': *The Great Meadow: Farmers and the Land in Colonial Concord*, New Haven: Yale University Press, 2004, pp. xi-xii.

[276] On these two GIS projects see Peter Bol, 'Creating a GIS for the History of China', in Knowles and Hillier (eds.), *Placing History*, pp. 27-60; Bernard Gauthiez and Olivier Zeller, 'Lyons, the Spatial Analysis of a City in the 17th and 18th Centuries: Locating and Crossing Data in a GIS Built from Written Sources', in Susanne Rau and Ekkehard Schönherr (eds.), *Mapping Spatial Relations, Their Perceptions and Dynamics: The City Today and in the Past*, Cham: Springer, 2014, pp. 97-118; see also Bernard Gauthiez, *The Production of Urban Space, Temporality, and Spatiality: Lyons, 1500-1900*, Berlin and Boston: De Gruyter, 2020.

[277] For a discussion of 'chorography', see Wigen, *A Malleable Map*, pp. 14-15; and della Dora, *Landscape, Nature, and the Sacred in Byzantium*, p. 11; see also the previous section on 'Cartographic Representations'.

[278] See Merrick Lex Berman, Ruth Mostern and Humphrey Southall (eds.), *Placing Names: Enriching and Integrating Gazetteers*, Bloomington: Indiana University Press, 2016; see also a detailed chapter by a major contributor to digital gazetteer development: Linda L. Hill, *Georeferencing: The*

gazetteer usually includes, at minimum, a name for a place, some designation of its 'type', and a spatial location. As is often the case for historical locations, however, any given place may have any number of names (or spellings of those names). Moreover, it may be classifiable according to multiple 'types' that are culturally or historically specific, and its location may not be well-established, subject to the contrary claims of differing sources or, indeed, physical relocation over time.

In the hands of historians, especially, digital gazetteers are important for their capacity to embrace this 'messiness'. Places may be recognised as standing in multiple relations to other places, hierarchically or otherwise, and any of its characteristics may be temporally delimited. Gazetteers may be deeply integrated with GIS applications and map visualisations, or they may be explored and analysed in their own right. Important collaborative projects such as the Pelagios Network and the World Historical Gazetteer have created new opportunities for integration between resources like the Pleiades Gazetteer of Past Places, the GeoNames geographical database, and other linked data sources.[279]

In one key respect, spatial history as HGIS is increasingly mirroring the rapid development of GIS methodologies in the social sciences. This can be seen in spatial history's use of the *analytical* tools on offer. Most HGIS practitioners use 'spatial analysis' as a synonym for the GIS term 'geospatial analysis': the application of statistical methods to geographic information. Ian Gregory has urged historians to move beyond 'crude spatial-pattern spotting' to fully embrace the potential of spatial statistics.[280] The work of Andrew Beveridge, for instance, shows how more advanced spatial statistics can be used to explore racial residential segregation over time in Chicago. Beveridge identifies a number of indexes that can be used to evaluate the degree of segregation. These include dissimilarity (the proportion of a community that

---

*Geographic Associations of Information*, Cambridge, Mass. and London: MIT Press, 2006, pp. 91-154.

[279] See HTTP: <https://pelagios.org/> (accessed 31 March 2021). They are also the author of the powerful tool Recogito, available HTTP: <https://recogito.pelagios.org/> (accessed 31 March 2021). The World Historical Gazetteer project is at HTTP: <http://whgazetteer.org/> (accessed 31 March 2021). Pleiades Gazetteer of Past Places, available HTTP: <http://pleiades.stoa.org/> (accessed 31 March 2021). GeoNames is a huge and publicly editable gazetteer of places, which aggregates place data from many sources. Available HTTP: <http://www.geonames.org/> (accessed 31 March 2021).

[280] See Gregory and Ell, *Historical GIS*, p. 118; see also his arguments in Ian N. Gregory, "'A Map is Just a Bad Graph": Why Spatial Statistics are Important in Historical GIS', in Knowles and Hillier (eds.), *Placing History*, pp. 123-50.

would need to move to equalise distribution over all units of space considered), exposure (proportion of non-majority groups present in a given spatial unit), and isolation (proportion of a group's total population in a given spatial unit).[281]

There is certainly no shortage of other methods and techniques. These include, for example, the algorithmic *interpolation* of historical data to rescale units of analysis or estimate data when it is unavailable. *Proximity analysis* and *spatial correlation* methods help to identify spatial patterns or clusters, while *watershed* and *visibility* analysis aims to explore historical rivers and land use or the limits of a visible landscape. Meanwhile, *cost path analysis* can facilitate an exploration of the optimum ways historical actors might move through roads or other spatially defined networks.[282]

The embrace of spatial statistics and the usually strong emphasis on disambiguation in the underlying data means that HGIS has had to face challenges to its theoretical foundations. Many of these challenges have emerged from the critical traditions of the discipline of geography itself.[283] David J. Bodenhamer has been a key figure in bringing much of this critical scholarship to the attention of HGIS practitioners. At the same time, he has proposed alternative 'deep mapping' approaches in the form of openly curated, non-static, spatial narratives that can help represent the contested nature of space and its fundamentally relational constitution.[284] However, the critical responses rarely advocate for a complete abandonment of GIS. As the impressive range of scholarship on display in the recent *Routledge Companion to*

---

[281] Andrew A. Beveridge, 'The Development, Persistence, and Change of Racial Segregation in U.S. Urban Areas 1880-2010', in Gregory and Geddes (eds.), *Toward Spatial Humanities*, pp. 35-61.

[282] See the chapters by Antonis Hadjikyriacou as well as Tim Cole and Alberto Giordano in Bavaj, Lawson and Struck (eds.), *Doing Spatial History* for examples of interpolation and cost path analysis. For a broader range of the techniques used in geospatial analysis see, for example, Michael J. de Smith, Michael F. Goodchild and Paul A. Longley, *Geospatial Analysis: A Comprehensive Guide to Principles, Techniques and Software Tools*, 6th ed., Leicester: Matador, 2018.

[283] The most important early contribution to this debate is John Pickles (ed.), *Ground Truth: The Social Implications of Geographic Information Systems*, New York: Guilford Press, 1995; see also Michael R. Curry, *Digital Places: Living with Geographic Information Technologies*, London: Routledge, 1998; and Matthew W. Wilson, *New Lines: Critical GIS and the Trouble of the Map*, Minneapolis: University of Minnesota Press, 2017.

[284] See David J. Bodenhamer, 'Narrating Space and Place', in David J. Bodenhamer, John Corrigan and Trevor M. Harris (eds.), *Deep Maps and Spatial Narratives*, Bloomington: Indiana University Press, 2015, pp. 7-27, here p. 21; id., 'The Potential of Spatial Humanities', in id., Corrigan and Harris (eds.), *The Spatial Humanities*, pp. 14-30, here pp. 14-20; see also the reflections in Alexander von Lünen and Charles Travis (eds.), *History and GIS: Epistemologies, Considerations and Reflections*, New York: Springer, 2013.

*Spatial History* suggests, spatial history imagined as HGIS is naturally a mixed methods approach. Alexander von Lünen goes one step further and advocates for the 'historian as bricoleur': someone who imaginatively and creatively tinkers with the tools at hand – including the visualization of historical narratives, or deep mapping – in order to accomplish a task for which those tools may not have been designed originally.[285]

## On the Great Plains

HGIS is still a young field. Geospatial analysis as deployed by geographers, while social scientists frequently make use of spatial statistical methodologies such as those mentioned above. To be sure, these have so far been less common in the work of historians.[286] However, even the act of overlaying multiple GIS layers of historical data can help visualise patterns impressive enough to shift the terms of major historical debates. A prominent example of this can be found in the form of Geoff Cunfer's award-winning *On the Great Plains: Agriculture and Environment* (2005) and its contribution to debates around the causes of the 1930s Dust Bowl.[287]

*On the Great Plains* explores the changing environment in over four hundred counties of the American Great Plains region from the 1870s until the late twentieth century. Its major source base comprises a collection of agricultural census data assembled by the Great Plains Population and Environment Project. This material allows Cunfer to methodically explore cultivation and grazing areas, crop diversity, irrigation patterns and agricultural mechanisation.[288] The vast majority of Cunfer's visualisations in the book come in the form of choropleth maps. These differently shade or colour particular spatial units – in this case, the counties from the case study – according to the value of a chosen variable. They are often combined into a series that captures different moments in time.

The maps find their most powerful use in chapter 6 ('Drought and Dust Bowl'). In this section of the book, Cunfer evaluates several theories of the

---

[285] Alexander von Lünen, 'Tracking in a New Territory: Re-Imaging GIS for History', in id. and Travis (eds.), *History and GIS*, pp. 211-39, here pp. 234-6.

[286] A fact lamented by Gregory, '"A Map is Just a Bad Graph"'.

[287] Geoff Cunfer, *On the Great Plains: Agriculture and Environment*, College Station: Texas A&M University Press, 2005. Cunfer's work engages that of Donald Worster, *Dust Bowl: The Southern Plains in the 1930s*, New York: Oxford University Press, 1979.

[288] 'Great Plains Population and Environment Data Series'. Available HTTP: <https://www.icpsr.umich.edu/web/DSDR/series/207> (accessed 31 March 2021).

reputed causes behind the 1930s economic and environmental Dust Bowl disaster. These have identified, variously, excessive cropland cultivation, erodible soils, and drought as the primary factors behind this catastrophe. The maps provided show the outlines of the area affected most heavily by dust storms in 1935-6, 1938, and 1940. These affected areas provide one layer of data which overlays a series of choropleth maps. These images display each relevant variable at key moments: the percentage of sandy soil; the percentage of counties devoted to crop land; rainfall levels in absolute terms or relative to the minimum required for a given crop; and temperature levels.[289]

The maps themselves, along with the accompanying analysis, do not depend on advanced spatial statistics. However, when they confront the reader with a visual representation of data from the massive and spatially rich database of agricultural census data, they are rhetorically compelling. Cunfer is able to show a lack of overlap between the reputed cause of the drought and the resulting damage. He is careful to note that the maps and their underlying data cannot eliminate other possibilities for which data is not available, such as the importance of wind or soil surface texture. Nonetheless, this GIS approach to studying the causes behind the Dust Bowl has left a powerful legacy.[290]

*On the Plains* was able to challenge the presumed explanatory power of several leading candidates for the primary cause of this important historical event. One claim, for example, held that the amount of cropland was the culprit. Cunfer, however, is able to show how, except for a portion of the Texas panhandle, drought appears to have played a particularly important role in the Dust Bowl. But the book is much more than a collection of maps and tables. Cunfer's quantitative analysis and maps work hand in hand with contemporary diaries and newspapers. These sources capture the lives of farmers at the time, but they also show that certain continuities were affected by dust storms in earlier periods. Cunfer's book thus offers a powerful example of the potential of HGIS to help shift historical debates around large-scale processes.

---

[289] Cunfer, *On the Great Plains*, pp. 154-5 on sandy soil, pp. 157-9 for rainfall, pp. 160-1 for temperatures.

[290] See Frank Uekötter, 'The Meaning of Moving Sand: Towards a Dust Bowl Mythology', *Global Environment* 8, 2015, 349-79, here 378.

# ABOUT THE AUTHORS

**Konrad Lawson** is Lecturer in Modern History, University of St Andrews, UK, and Co-Director of the Institute for Transnational and Spatial History. His research focuses on modern East Asian history and the aftermaths of Japanese empire.

**Riccardo Bavaj** is Professor of Modern History, University of St Andrews, UK, and Co-Director of the Institute for Transnational and Spatial History. His research focuses on the intellectual and spatial history of twentieth-century Germany. He has co-edited Germany and 'the West' and Zivilisatorische Verortungen (with Martina Steber).

**Bernhard Struck** is Reader of Modern History, University of St Andrews, UK, and Founding Director of the Institute for Transnational and Spatial History. His research focuses on continental European History, c.1750 to early twentieth-century, comparative and transnational history. He has co-edited Shaping the Transnational Sphere (with Davide Rodogno and Jakob Vogel).

Printed in Great Britain
by Amazon

76158822R00061